EXAMINING CONCEPTS IN SEXUALITY

D1278545

2nd edition

Rosemary Iconis, Ed. D.
The City University of New York

TIMBER HOUSE BOOKS

Examining Concepts in Sexuality 2nd Edition

CONTENTS

Part I

INTRODUCTION TO
THE STUDY OF HUMAN
SEXUALITY

WORKSHEET #1

Why Study Sexuality?

Few topics grab our attention and spark our interest the way the topic of sex can. Aspects of sexuality – how we relate to those we love, whether or not we have children, how we express ourselves as males or females – are among the most essential characteristics of our lives. In many respects, they define who we are.

Sexuality is a complex area of study that includes biological, psychological, sociocultural, and political dimensions. The multiple dimensions of sexuality impact us throughout our lives.

Most students study sexuality, at least partly, to increase their sexual health. Sexual health encompasses understanding yourself sexually, enhancing your ability to relate in a sexual relationship, recognizing that each person expresses sexuality in his or her own way, and adding to your accurate sexual knowledge.

WORKSHEET #2

Sexual Knowledge

Most parents agree that one of their most important functions is to try to keep their children safe from harm. Parents often teach their young children to look both ways before crossing a street. They might teach their adolescents about the dangers of drug abuse.

One out of four sexually active teenagers will contract a sexually transmitted infection before they are eighteen. The U.S. teen pregnancy rates are among the highest of any industrialized nation (Weinstock et al., 2004). Adolescents in the United States don't begin having sex at an earlier age than adolescents in other industrialized nations nor do they have significantly more sex. Yet teens in the U.S. are getting pregnant and contracting STI's much more than teens in other developed countries. Teens in the U.S. are much less likely to use contraceptives and much more likely to have more sexual partners than their counterparts around the developed world. Still, many parents are embarrassed and uncomfortable talking to their children about sex. As a result, friends, and to a lesser extent, the media are the principal sources of information about sex for young people in the United States (Sprecher et al., 2008). Sources such as friends, movies, television shows, and the Internet are all subject to misinformation and the perpetration of myths.

To get a brief overview of how much sexual knowledge you already possess, complete the following test. Mark each of the statements, true (T) or false (F).

_____ 1. On average, it takes 12 to 18 months to become pregnant after discontinuing use of the birth control pill.

_____ 2. Seventy-five percent of Americans are not virgins when they get married.

_____ 3. It is not possible for a woman to give birth to a baby with fetal alcohol syndrome unless the woman is an alcoholic.

_____ 4. One in every 10 people diagnosed with AIDS in the U.S. is over the age of 50.

_____ 5. Male circumcision reduces the rate of HPV transmission and HIV transmission.

_____ 6. Until 1993, it was legal in some states for a man to rape his wife.

WORKSHEET #2 (CONTINUED)

_____ 7. A woman cannot become pregnant during her menstrual period.

_____ 8. When it comes to falling in love and marrying, generally "opposites attract."

_____ 9. Abortion rates are often highest in countries where abortion is highly restricted.

_____ 10. Transvestites (cross-dressers) are almost always heterosexual males.

WORKSHEET #3

Classifying Sexual Behavior

When studying sexuality, at some point, most students will ask the fundamental question, "Am I normal?" It is difficult to define normal sexual behavior because so many factors must be considered. Normality is influenced by cultural, generational, and personal factors. It's also difficult to avoid sounding judgmental when addressing the issue of normality. A number of strategies can be used to address the issue. Some researchers describe sexual behavior as existing on a continuum between normal and abnormal. Another approach is to consider various categories to define normality.

For example:

- *Subjective Normality* -This standard asserts that "I am normal so anyone like me is normal."
- *Statistical Normality* -This standard is based on the number of people engaging in a given behavior.
- *Psychological Normality* -This standard is based on the absence of anxiety, guilt, or frustration.
- *Moral Normality* - This standard is based within a cultural, historical, or religious context.

In the spaces below, indicate whether you believe each activity listed is: natural/unnatural, normal/abnormal, or moral/immoral.

Natural (Y = Yes; N = No) Moral (Y = Yes; N = No)
    Natural   Moral

_____ _____ 1. Remaining a virgin until marriage

_____ _____ 2. Having sex with two or more partners at the same time

_____ _____ 3. Having anal sex

_____ _____ 4. Watching pornographic films

_____ _____ 5. Having typically male <u>and</u> female characteristics

_____ _____ 6. Becoming sexually active before the age of 15

_____ _____ 7. Having rape fantasies

WORKSHEET #3 (CONTINUED)

Natural (Y = Yes; N = No)   Moral (Y = Yes; N = No)
   Natural   Moral

_____ _____ 8. Using sex toys

_____ _____ 9. Having sexual contact with an animal

_____ _____ 10. Participating in surrogacy

       (having a woman carry a baby to term for another woman or couple)

_____ _____ 11. Having sex without emotional involvement

_____ _____ 12. Masturbating

_____ _____ 13. Inflicting pain or humiliation on someone for sexual gratification

_____ _____ 14. Transitioning from male to female or female to male

       (i.e. transgender sexual reassignment)

_____ _____ 15. Having sex in public

_____ _____ 16. Being sexually attracted to someone of the same sex

_____ _____ 17. Choosing not to have children

_____ _____ 18. Being sexually gratified by dressing as a member of the other sex

_____ _____ 19. Remaining sexually active into old age

_____ _____ 20. Lacking sexual desire

_____ _____ 21. Having a romantic relationship with someone more than 15 years older than you

_____ _____ 22. Being sexually attracted to minors

WORKSHEET #4

Methods for Studying Sexuality

Case Study: This is the examination of an individual subject or group of subjects.

Survey Method: Data pertaining to sexual attitudes and behaviors of relatively large groups of subjects is collected by means of interviews or questionnaires.

Observational Method: The investigators directly observe sexual behavior. The physiological responses of the subjects are monitored and recorded.

Experimental Method: Strict control is maintained over all variables so that one variable can be isolated and examined.

Method	Advantage	Disadvantage
Case Study		
Survey Method		
Observational Method		
Experimental Method		

WORKSHEET #4 (CONTINUED)

Most of our information about human sexuality has been obtained from the survey method of research. Surveys can be conducted orally, as in interviews, or through questionnaires.

Whether conducted as an interview or a questionnaire, the survey method tries to use a relatively small group, called the survey sample, to draw inferences or conclusions about a much larger group with a particular defining feature, called a target population. An example of a target population is college freshman.

Usually, researchers hope to select a representative sample, which is a type of limited research sample that provides an accurate representation of the larger target population. If the procedures to obtain a representative sample are applied correctly, one can be reasonably confident that the findings of the research will be able to be generalized to the entire target population. Another type of sample, a random sample, is one in which each member of the target population has an equal probability of participating. A random sample may or may not be the same as a representative sample.

Typically, representative samples allow for more accurate generalizations to the entire target population than do random samples. Still, both types of samples are used widely in sex surveys.

———————————

Problems of Sex Survey Research

1. Nonresponse_____

2. Self-selection _____

3. Demographic bias_____

4. Accuracy of subjects' responses_____

PART I: READING

The Tuskegee Syphilis Study

On July 25, 1972 the Washington Evening Star newspaper ran this headline on its front page: "Syphilis Patients Died Untreated." With those words, one of America's most notorious medical studies, the Tuskegee Syphilis Study, became public.

"For 40 years, the U.S. Public Health Service has conducted a study in which human guinea pigs, not given proper treatment, have died of syphilis and its side effects," Associated Press reporter Jean Heller wrote on July 25, 1972. The study was conducted to determine from autopsies what the disease does to the human body."

The next morning, every major U.S. newspaper was running Heller's story.

The Study

In 1932, the Public Health Service, working with the Tuskegee Institute, began a study to record the natural history of syphilis in hopes of justifying treatment programs for blacks. It was called the "Tuskegee Study of Untreated Syphilis in the Negro Male."

The study involved 399 poor black men with syphilis. The study was conducted without the benefit of patients' informed consent. Researchers told the men they were being treated for "bad blood," a local term used to describe several ailments, including syphilis, anemia, and fatigue. In truth, they did not receive the proper treatment needed to cure their illness. In exchange for taking part in the study, the men received free medical exams, free meals, and burial insurance. Although originally projected to last six months, the study actually went on for forty years.

At the start of the study, there was no proven treatment for syphilis. But even after penicillin became a standard cure for the disease in 1947, the medicine was withheld from the men. The Tuskegee scientists wanted to continue to study how the disease spreads and kills. By then, dozens of the men had died, and many wives and children had been infected.

PART I: READING (CONTINUED)

The Story Is Leaked to the Media

In July of 1972, a public health worker leaked the story to the media. An Associated Press Story about the Tuskegee Study caused a public outcry that led the Assistant Secretary for Health and Scientific Affairs to appoint an Ad Hoc Advisory Panel to review the study. The panel had nine members from the fields of medicine, law, religion, labor, education, health administration, and public affairs.

The panel found that the men had agreed freely to be examined and treated. However, there was no evidence that researchers had informed them of the study or its real purpose. In fact, the men had been misled and had not been given all the facts required to provide informed consent.

The men were never given adequate treatment for their disease. Even when penicillin became the drug of choice for syphilis in 1947, researchers did not offer it to the subjects. The advisory panel found nothing to show that subjects were ever given the choice of quitting the study, even when this new, highly effective treatment became widely used.

The advisory panel concluded that the Tuskegee Study was "ethically unjustified" – the knowledge gained was sparse when compared with the risks the study posed for its subjects. In October 1972, the panel advised stopping the study at once. A month later, the Assistant Secretary for Health and Scientific Affairs announced the end of the Tuskegee Study.

Reparation Begins

In 1973, The National Association for the Advancement of Colored People (NAACP) filed a class-action lawsuit on behalf of the study participants and their families. In 1974, a $10 million out of court settlement was reached. As part of the settlement, the U.S. government promised to give lifetime medical benefits and burial services to all living participants. The Tuskegee Health Benefit Program (THBP) was established to provide these services.

In 1975, wives, widows and offspring were added to the program. In 1995, the program was expanded to include health as well as medical benefits. The Centers for Disease Control and Prevention was given responsibility for the program.

Tuskegee Changed Research Practices

After the Tuskegee Study, the government changed its research practices to prevent a repeat of the mistakes made in Tuskegee.

PART I: READING (CONTINUED)

In 1974, the National Research Act was signed into law, creating the National Commission for the Protection of Human Subjects of Biomedical and Behavioral Research. The group identified basic principles of research conduct and suggested ways to ensure those principles are followed.

An Apology

It wasn't until 1997 that the government formally apologized for the unethical study.

President Clinton delivered the apology, saying what the government had done was deeply, profoundly and morally wrong.

> *"To the survivors, to the wives and family members, the children and the grandchildren, I say what you know: no power on Earth can give you back the lives lost, the pain suffered, the years of internal torment and anguish."*

> *"What was done cannot be undone. We can end the silence. We can stop turning our heads away. We can look at you in the eye and finally say, on behalf of the American people: what the United States government did was shameful. And I am sorry."*

PART I: READING (CONTINUED)

NAME _____

"It's very easy for a number of people to think that "Well, since that (Tuskegee) 'happened,'… a number of people have the idea that there is always that possibility that people who are disadvantaged may be used as guinea pigs in terms of medicine," said Thomas Blocker, Director of Health Professions at Morehouse College.

There are now regulations in place designed to ensure the ethical treatment of research subjects. Still, do you feel that socioeconomic/racial/gender discrimination exists when it comes to medical care in the U.S? (Be as specific as possible)

_____

_____

_____

_____

_____

_____

_____

_____

_____

_____

_____

_____

_____

_____

REFERENCES

Centers for Disease Control and Prevention. *U.S. Public Health Service Syphilis Study at Tuskegee.* Last reviewed June 14, 2011. Web. 18 Nov. 2012. ‹http://www.cdc.gov/Tuskegee/timeline.htm›

Centers for Disease Control and Prevention. *U.S. Public Health Service Study at Tuskegee (Research Implications).* Last reviewed June 14, 2011. Web. 18 Nov. 2012. ‹http://www.cdc.gov/Tuskegee/after.htm›

National Public Radio. *Remembering Tuskegee.* July 25, 2002. Web 28 Nov. 2012. ‹http://www.npr.org/programs/morning/features/2002/jul/Tuskegee/›

Sprecher, S., Harris, G., and Meyers, A. (2008). Perceptions of sources of sex education and targets of communication: sociodemographic and cohort effects. *Journal of Sex Research*, 44, 17-26.

Weinstock, H., Berman, S., and Cates, W. (2004). Sexually transmitted diseases among American youth: incidences and prevalence estimates, 2000. *Perspectives on Sexual and Reproductive Health*, 36(1), 6-10.

PART II

FEMALE REPRODUCTIVE ANATOMY AND PHYSIOLOGY

WORKSHEET #5

External Female Anatomy

The external female genitalia, or vulva, include the mons veneris or mons pubis, the labia, the clitoris, and the urethral and vaginal openings.

Components of the Vulva

The **mons pubis** is the pad of fat that covers, cushions, and protects the pubic joint. At puberty, rising levels of androgens promote the growth of pubic hair over the mons pubis.

The **labia majora** are two longitudinal folds of fatty tissue that extend from the mons to the perineum (the tissue between the vagina and the anus). The skin of the outer labia majora is pigmented and covered with hair, whereas the inner surface is hairless. During sexual excitement, the labia majora fill with blood and engorge, which makes the entire pubic region seem to swell.

The smaller, hairless **labia minora** are located between the labia majora. These inner lips run from the hood of the clitoris down either side of the urethral and vaginal openings. The color and appearance of the labia minora vary from woman to woman.

The **clitoris** is the small sensitive tissue located behind the junction of the labia minora. The clitoris consists of erectile tissue with a glans, a shaft, and crura. Analogous to the penis, the clitoris has a rich supply of blood vessels and nerve endings. While much smaller than the average penis, the clitoris contains twice as many nerve endings.

The **clitoral glans** is extremely sensitive to sexual stimulation. It's only known function is sexual arousal. The glans is covered by the **clitoral hood** or **prepuce**, which is the area where the labia minora meets at the top.

Smegma can accumulate under the hood, causing an unpleasant odor. Women can prevent its formation by drawing back the prepuce to clean underneath. The **shaft** is made up of erectile tissue that fills with blood when a woman is aroused. As the shaft progresses deeper into the woman's body it splits into two forks, called **crura**, which extend along either side of the vaginal opening and attach to the pelvic bones. The **vestibule** is the name for the entire region between the labia minora and can be clearly seen when the labia are held apart. The vestibule contains the opening of the urethra and the vagina and the ducts of Bartholin's glands.

WORKSHEET #5 (CONTINUED)

The *vestibule* is the name for the entire region between the labia minora and can be clearly seen when the labia are held apart. The vestibule contains the opening of the urethra and the vagina and the ducts of Bartholin's glands.

The *urethral meatus* is the opening to the urethra. The meatus lies between the vagina and clitoris. The urethra, which brings urine from the bladder to be eliminated is much shorter in women than in men, in whom it runs the length of the penis. A shorter urethra allows bacteria greater access to the urinary tract, making women much more susceptible to *urinary tract infections (UTIs).* Common symptoms for UTIs include pain or burning in the urethra or bladder and an increased urge to urinate. Antibiotics are necessary to cure the infection. Research has shown that consuming cranberry products (i.e. drinks, breads) may be effective in decreasing UTI recurrence.

The entrance, or *introitus,* of the vagina also lies in the vestibule. The introitus is usually covered at birth by a fold of tissue known as the *hymen*. The center of the hymen is usually perforated, and it is through this perforation that the menstrual flow leaves the vagina. If the hymen is intact, it will usually rupture easily and tear at several points during the first sexual intercourse, often accompanied by a small amount of blood.

An intact hymen has been a sign throughout history that a woman has not engaged in sexual intercourse. In reality, many activities can tear the hymen, including vigorous exercise, horseback or bike riding, masturbation, or the insertion of tampons. Still, in many cultures, the absence of bloodstained bed sheets on the wedding night is enough to condemn a woman for not being a virgin.

The *Bartholin's glands* are bean-shaped glands with ducts that empty into the vestibule in the middle of the labia minora. They secrete fluid into the vestibule during sexual arousal, although the major source of lubrication is fluid from blood vessels within the vaginal walls.

WORKSHEET #6

The Vulva (external female Anatomy)

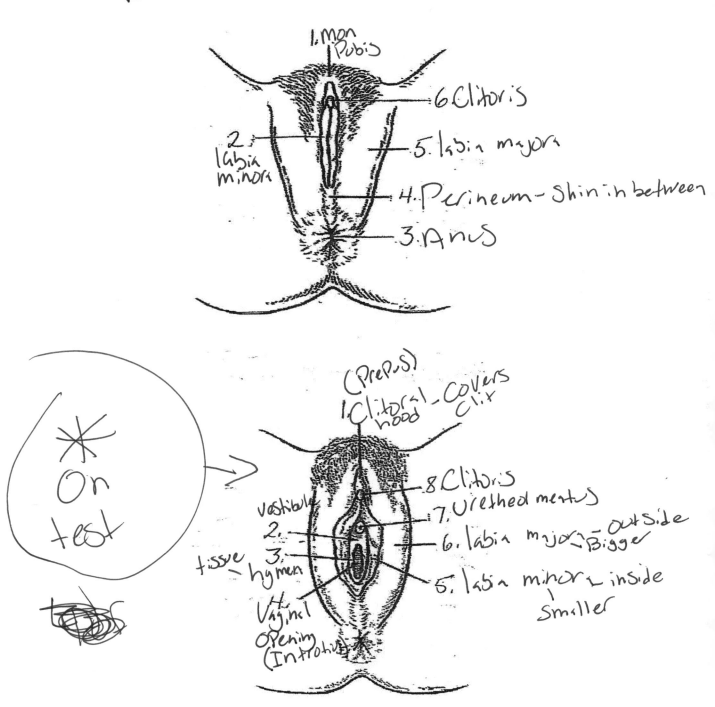

1. Mon Pubis
6 Clitoris
2. labia minora
5. labia majora
4. Perineum - Shin in between
3. Anus

(Prepus)
1. Clitoral hood - covers clit
★ On test
vestibule
2.
3. hymen
tissue
8 Clitoris
7. Urethral meatus
6. labia majora - outside - Bigger
5. labia minora - inside - Smaller
4. Vaginal Opening (Introitus)

WORKSHEET #7

Internal Female Anatomy

The Vagina

The *vagina* is located between the rectum and the urethra. It is a collapsible tube of smooth muscle, three to five inches long when relaxed. It serves as a passageway for menstrual fluid, a depository for sperm, and as the birth canal. The inner lining of the walls is a mucous membrane containing folds that stimulate the penis during intercourse. The middle layer of the walls is composed of smooth muscle. Although smooth muscles are capable of powerful contractions, they are not subject to voluntary control. When a woman is aroused, blood rushes to the vagina. Fluid (not blood) from the capillaries crosses the vaginal walls, protecting the vagina by preventing vaginal tearing during intercourse. The vagina can expand to accommodate a penis during intercourse and can stretch four to five times its normal size during childbirth.

Although the first third of the vagina is well endowed with nerve endings, the inner two thirds are practically without sensation. A spot about the size of a quarter in the first third of the vagina, the *Gräfenberg spot (G-spot)*, was first described by Ernest Gräfenberg in 1950. The G-spot is found about two or three inches up on the front (or stomach) side of the vagina, just past the pubic bone. The G-spot is thought to be an area that, when stimulated, produces powerful orgasms.

A healthy vagina contains *lactobacteria*, which prevent the growth of harmful bacteria. Lactobacteria increase the acidity of the vagina, killing most of the sperm deposited during sexual intercourse. A number of things destroy the helpful lactobacteria and disturb the vaginal flora. Douching, antibiotics, hormones, stress, STIs, and poor hygiene can all upset the delicate balance of organisms in the vagina which can lead to common vaginal infections.

Note: The *pubococcygeus (PC) muscle* stretches from the pubic bone to the coccyx, surrounding the urethral, vaginal, and anal openings and supporting a number of organs. Rhythmic clenching and unclenching of the PC muscles are called *Kegel exercises*. They're done to help prevent incontinence and, possibly, to increase the strength of orgasm.

The Uterus

The *uterus* is a thick-walled, hollow, muscular organ in the pelvis located between the bladder in front and the rectum behind. The uterus is held in place by ligaments and moves inside the body depending on the woman's position or the fullness of her bladder. The uterus of a woman who has never been pregnant is about the size of a small fist, and weighs about two ounces.

WORLD WORKSHEET #7 (CONTINUED)

The ***cervix*** is the lower end of the uterus that leads into the vagina. The opening of the cervix, called the ***os***, is normally covered by a mucous plug. During childbirth, the os will expand to four inches and the mucous plug will be released.

The inner lining of the uterus is called the ***endometrium***. The lining will thicken each month in anticipation of conception. If a fertilized egg is not deposited in the endometrium, the lining is shed as menstrual flow. Layers of smooth muscle make up the thick middle layer called the ***myometrium***. The outermost ***perimetrium*** is a membrane that covers the body of the uterus. It helps to keep the uterus cushioned.

The uterus is home to the developing fetus. If fertilization occurs, the fertilized egg implants in the endometrial lining, where it continues its development. During labor, strong contractions of the myometrial layer expel the fetus through the vaginal birth canal and out of the body. The uterus secretes many substances which help to maintain the developing fetus. The uterus also makes *prostaglandins*, which contract the uterus and widen the cervix during labor.

The Fallopian Tubes

Fallopian tubes, or ***oviducts***, are four-inch long tubes that extend laterally from the sides of the uterus. The tube expands into an ampulla, which curves around to a trumpet shaped end, called the ***infundibulum***. At the end of the infundibulum are finger-like projections that curl around the ovary ready to accept ***ova*** when they are released.

Fallopian tubes are not directly attached to the ovaries. They open into the abdominal cavity very close to each ovary. Long, fingerlike projections called ***fimbriae*** extend toward the ovary without actually touching it. After an ovum, or egg, is released from the ovary during ovulation, it enters and travels through the Fallopian tube where it may be fertilized by sperm.

The inner surfaces of the Fallopian tubes are covered by cilia (hair-like projections); the constant beating action of the cilia creates a current along which the ovum is moved toward the uterus. The entire transit time from ovulation until arrival inside the uterus is normally about three days.

And ***ectopic pregnancy*** occurs when the fertilized egg implants outside of the uterus most often in the fallopian tubes.

WORKSHEET #7 (CONTINUED)

The Ovaries

The mature ovary is a light gray structure most commonly described as the size and shape of an almond shell. With age, the ovaries become smaller and firmer. The ovaries have two responsibilities: to produce ova and to secrete hormones.

Within the ovary are **oocytes**, also known as ova, or eggs. A female is born with approximately 250,000 ova in each ovary, each sitting in its own primary follicle. The primary follicle contains an immature ovum surrounded by a thin layer of follicular cells. Follicle-stimulating hormone (FSH) and luteinizing hormone (LH) are released by the pituitary gland during each menstrual cycle, causing about 20 primary follicles at a time to begin maturing. Usually only one follicle finishes maturing each month, which is then termed a *secondary follicle*, containing a secondary oocyte. At ovulation, the secondary follicle bursts, and the ovum begins its journey down the Fallopian tube. Once released, the ovum remains viable for fertilization for approximately 24 hours.

Ovulation can occur each month from either the right or left ovary. No one knows why one or the other ovary releases an ovum any given month. If one ovary is removed, however, the other ovary will often ovulate every month. The ovaries are also the female's most important producer of female sex hormones, such as estrogen.

WORKSHEET #8

Internal Female Anatomy (Diagram)

Menarchy – First time women menstrate)

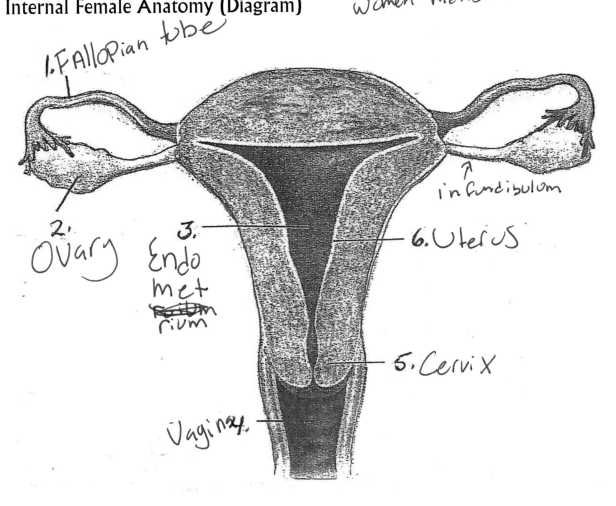

1. FAllopian tube

infundibulom

2. Ovary

3. Endo met rium

6. Uterus

5. Cervix

Vagina.

OVvulation – egg matures & is released by ovary

WORKSHEET #9

The Breasts

Anatomy of the Breast

Each breast has 15 to 20 sections, called lobes, which are arranged like the petals of a daisy. Each lobe has many smaller lobules, which end in dozens of tiny bulbs that can produce milk. The lobes, lobules, and bulbs are all linked by thin tubes called ducts. These ducts lead to the nipple in the center of a dark area of skin called the areola. Fat fills the spaces between lobules and ducts. There are no muscles in the breast, but muscles lie under each breast and cover the ribs.

Each breast also contains blood vessels and lymph vessels. The lymph vessels lead to small bean-shaped organs called lymph nodes, clusters of which are found under the arm, above the collarbone, and in the chest, as well as in many other parts of the body.

What breast changes happen at puberty?

Breasts begin to form during fetal development. By the time a female infant is born, a nipple and the beginnings of the milk-duct system have formed. As a girl approaches adolescence, the first outward signs of breast development begin to appear. When the ovaries start to secrete estrogen, fat in the connective tissue begins to accumulate causing the breasts to enlarge. The duct system also begins to grow. Usually the onset of these breast changes is also accompanied by the appearance of pubic hair and hair under the arms.

Once ovulation and menstruation begin, the maturing of the breasts begins with the formation of secretory glands at the end of the milk ducts. The breasts and duct system continue to grow and mature, with the development of many glands and lobules. The rate at which breasts grow varies greatly and is different for each young woman.

What happens to the breast at menopause?

By the time a woman reaches her late 40s and early 50s, menopause is beginning or is well underway. At this time, levels of estrogen dramatically decrease. This leads to many of the symptoms commonly associated with menopause (vaginal dryness; hot flashes). With this reduction in estrogen stimulation to all tissues of the body, including the breast tissue, there is a reduction in the glandular tissue of the breasts. Without estrogen, the connective tissue of the breast becomes dehydrated and inelastic, and the breast tissue shrinks and loses shape. This leads to the "sagging" of the breasts often associated with women of this age.

WORKSHEET #10

Common Benign (Non-cancerous) Breast Lumps

benign - non cancer
malignant - cancerous
Metastasis - spreads

Cysts - almost never cancerous

*A cyst is a fluid-filled sac in the breast tissue. Cysts typically occur in women between the ages of 35 and 50 and are most common in those approaching menopause. They often enlarge and become tender and painful just before the menstrual period. Cysts are rarely malignant and may be caused by a blockage of breast glands.

Cysts can feel either soft or hard. When close to the surface of the breast, cysts can feel like a large blister, smooth on the outside, but fluid-filled on the inside. However, when they are deeply embedded in breast tissue, cysts will feel like hard lumps because they are covered with tissue.

A healthcare provider may identify a lump as a cyst by physical examination, but many healthcare providers confirm the diagnosis by mammography or ultrasound examination. The healthcare provider may then draw some fluid from the cyst (fine-needle aspiration) as the next step in diagnosing it. This procedure also serves as the treatment for this condition, as once the cyst is aspirated, it collapses and disappears. Cysts can reappear at a later date, in which case they are simply drained again. Cysts are seldom malignant.

Fibroadenomas - benign tumors   Breasts/Uterus

*Fibroadenomas are solid, firm, benign lumps that are most commonly found in women in their 20s and 30s. They are the most common benign lumps that occur in women and can occur in women of any age. Fibroadenomas vary in size and can grow anywhere in the breast tissue.

While most healthcare providers can recognize this type of lump simply by feeling it, generally, the diagnosis is confirmed by mammography or ultrasound and fine-needle aspiration. Sometimes, in very young women, the fibroadenoma is not removed. However, since sometimes these tumors enlarge with pregnancy and breast-feeding, healthcare providers may recommend its surgical removal.

WORKSHEET #11

Breast Cancer *— one of most common cancers in women*

Men can get Breast Cancer

According to the Centers for Disease Control and Prevention (2013), not counting some kinds of skin cancer, breast cancer in the United States is:

- *✱* The most common cancer in women, no matter your race or ethnicity
- The most common cause of death from cancer among Hispanic women
- The second most common cause of death from cancer among white, black, Asian/Pacific Islander, and American Indian/Alaskan native women

✱ Men can get breast cancer. In men, breast cancer can happen at any age, but is most common in men who are between 60 and 70 years old. Male breast cancer is not very common. For every 100 cases of breast cancer, less than one is in men.

Risk Factors

Researchers found several risk factors that may increase your chances of getting breast cancer.

Reproductive Risk Factors *— Come from estrogen*

- Getting your first menstrual period early in life
- Starting menopause at a later age
- Being older at the birth of your first child
- Never giving birth
- Long-term use of hormone-replacement therapy

Other Risk Factors

- Getting older
- Personal history of breast cancer
- Family history of breast cancer (mother, father, sister, brother, daughter, or son)
- Treatment with radiation therapy to the breast/chest
- Being overweight (increases risk for breast cancer after menopause)
- Changes in the breast cancer-related genes BRCA1 or BRCA2 (approximately 5 to 10% of breast and ovarian cancers are due to predisposing genetic factors)

WORKSHEET #11 (CONTINUED)

- Drinking alcohol (more than one drink a day)
- Not getting regular exercise

Signs or Symptoms

While some people do not have any signs or symptoms at all some warning signs of breast cancer are:

- New lump in the breast or underarm (It is recommended that women perform a monthly breast self-examination)
- Thickening or swelling of part of the breast
- Irritation or dimpling of breast skin
- Redness or flaky skin in the nipple area or in the breast
- Pulling in of the nipple or pain in the nipple area
- Nipple discharge other than breast-milk
- Any change in the size or the shape of the breast
- Pain in any area of the breast

Keep in mind that some of these warning signs can happen with other conditions that are not cancer.

Screening and Diagnostic Tests Include:

- **Breast ultrasound.** A machine uses sound waves to make detailed pictures, called sonograms, of areas inside the breast
- **Mammogram.** Screening mammograms are done for purposes of early detection and prompt treatment. If an area of the breast looks abnormal on a screening mammogram, doctors may suggest a diagnostic mammogram. This is a more detailed x-ray of the breast.
- **Magnetic resonance imaging (MRI).** This is a kind of body scan that uses a magnet linked to a computer. The MRI scan will make detailed pictures of areas inside the breast.
- **Biopsy.** This is a test that removes tissue or fluid from the breast to be looked at under a microscope.

Treatment

Breast cancer is treated in several ways. It depends on the kind of breast cancer and if it has spread.

WORKSHEET #11 (CONTINUED)

Treatment Options Include:

- **Surgery.** An operation where doctors cut out and remove cancer tissue
- **Chemotherapy.** This is using special drugs to shrink or kill the cancer. The drugs can be pills you take or medicines given through an intravenous (IV) tube, or, sometimes, both.
- **Hormonal therapy.** Some cancers need certain hormones to grow. Hormonal treatment is used to block cancer cells from getting the hormones they need to grow.
- **Biological therapy.** This treatment works with your body's immune system to help it fight cancer or to control side effects from other cancer treatments. Biological therapy is different from chemotherapy, which attacks cancer cells directly.
- **Radiation.** This is the use of high-energy rays to kill the cancer cells. The rays are aimed at the part of the body where the cancer is located.

WORKSHEET #12

BRCA₁ and BRCA₂: Cancer Risk and Genetic Testing

- Just first

- BRCA$_1$ and BRCA$_2$ are human genes that belong to a class of genes known as tumor suppressors. Mutation of these genes has been linked to hereditary breast and ovarian cancer. Everyone carries the BRCA$_1$ and BRCA$_2$ genes.

- A woman's risk of developing breast and/or ovarian cancer is greatly increased if she inherits a harmful copy, or mutation. Less than 1% of women have the mutation. Men with these mutations also have an increased risk of breast cancer. Both men and women who have harmful BRCA$_1$ or BRCA$_2$ mutations may be at increased risk of other cancers.

- Genetic tests are available to check for BRCA$_1$ and BRCA$_2$ mutations. It can be detected by a blood test or a saliva test. Genetic counseling is recommended before and after the tests.

- A woman's lifetime risk of developing breast and/or ovarian cancer is greatly increased if she inherits a harmful mutation in BRCA$_1$ or BRCA$_2$. Such a woman has an increased risk of developing breast and/or ovarian cancer at an early age (before menopause) and often has multiple, close family members who have been diagnosed with these diseases. Harmful BRCA$_1$ mutations may also increase a woman's risk of developing cervical, uterine, pancreatic, and colon cancer. Harmful BRCA$_2$ mutations may additionally increase the risk of pancreatic cancer, stomach cancer, gallbladder and bile duct cancer, and melanoma.

- According to estimates of lifetime risk, about 12% of women (120 out of 1,000) in the general population will develop breast cancer sometime during their lives compared with about 60% of women (600 out of 1,000) who have inherited a harmful mutation in BRCA$_1$ or BRCA$_2$. In other words, a woman who has inherited a harmful mutation in BRCA$_1$ or BRCA2 is about five times more likely to develop breast cancer than a woman who does not have such a mutation.

- If a harmful BRCA$_1$ or BRCA$_2$ mutation is found, several options are available to help a person manage their cancer risk, including the surgical removal of the breasts and ovaries (National Cancer Institute, 2009).

WORKSHEET #13

Breast Cancer Prevention  Just Bullet

Lifestyle changes have been shown to decrease breast cancer risk.

- **Maintain a healthy weight**

  _____

  _____

- **Exercise regularly**

  _____

  _____

- **Minimize alcohol**

  _____

  _____

- **Limit fat intake**

  _____

  _____

- **Eat a diet rich in fruits and vegetables**

  _____

  _____

- **Include foods rich in omega-3 fatty acids in your diet**

_____

_____

- **Keep hydrated**

_____

_____

The Isoflavone Question

Phytoestrogens are a group of plant-derived compounds that are structurally similar to estrogen. There are several different groups of phytoestrogens; the most widely studied are the isoflavones, present in high concentrations in soy products such as soybeans, tofu, and soy milk. When it comes to breast cancer, there has been some evidence that soy can play a protective role; however, its effects may depend on when in life it's consumed.

It's been proposed that isoflavones may act as anti-estrogens in premenopausal women who have high circulating hormone levels. But after menopause, when estrogen levels are low, they may mimic estrogen. An estrogen boost, even if weak, may be harmful in such women. The optimal amount of dietary soy is unknown. The topic is still a controversial one in the medical literature.

WORKSHEET #14

Myth or Fact

1. Most lumps in the breast are cancerous.

   Myth 8/10 Benign

2. Breast self-examination should be done during menstruation.

   Myth Week after

3. Breast implants have no effect on mammograms.

   Myth not true make it harder to read

4. Small breasted women produce less milk than large breasted women.

   Myth Nothing to do With breast size

5. The primary function of the breast is sexual attraction.

   Myth feed the yong

6. Breast cancer does not develop in women under the age of 40.

   Myth not Common but can happen

7. Research has shown that the use of antiperspirants increases a woman's risk for breast cancer.

   Myth Not true No research

8. Doctors are not permitted to perform breast augmentation surgery (breast enlargement) on girls 18 years of age or younger.

   Myth Not illegal

WORKSHEET #15

Gynecologic Cancers

Uterine Cancer

✳It is the fourth most common cancer in women in the United States and the most commonly diagnosed gynecologic cancer.

Risk factors include:

- **Age** - most cases occur in women who are going through or have gone through menopause
- **Prolonged exposure to estrogen**
- **High-fat diet**
- **Obesity**

Cervical Cancer

✳It is the only gynecological cancer for which there is a screening test - the Pap test

Precancrous
abnormalities in cells
in cervix

Risk factors include:

- **Having multiple partners** - because of increased risk of contracting HPV
- **Smoking**
- **Family history**

Ovarian Cancer

*~ more deaths 1. Where ovaries are located(hard to get too)
2. no good screening test
3. symptoms are vague*

✳About 90% of women who get ovarian cancer are older than 40 years of age. Even though ovarian cancer accounts for only about 3% of all cancers in women, it causes more deaths than any other gynecologic cancer.

Risk factors include:

- Prolonged exposure to estrogen
- High fat diet
- Obesity
- Family history

WORKSHEET #15 (CONTINUED)

Since there is no simple and reliable way to screen for any gynecologic cancers except cervical cancer, it is especially important to recognize warning signs and symptoms.

Gynecologic Cancer Symptoms			
Symptoms	**Cervical Cancer**	**Ovarian Cancer**	**Uterine Cancer**
Abnormal vaginal bleeding or discharge	●	●	●
Pelvic pain or pressure		●	●
Abdominal or back pain		●	
Bloating		●	

SOURCE: Centers for Disease Control and Prevention, 2010

WORKSHEET #16

Phases of the Menstrual Cycle

Every month between puberty and menopause, a female's body prepares for pregnancy. The average cycle is 28 days, although it can vary greatly from woman to woman and month to month. The phases are: the follicular phase, ovulation, the luteal phase, and the menstrual phase. Day one of the cycle is considered to be the first day of the menstrual period.

The Follicular Phase

- Usually lasts from day 6 through 13

- Gonadotropin-releasing hormone (GnRH) is released by the hypothalamus; this, in turn, results in rising levels of follicle-stimulating hormone (FSH) and estrogen.

- As a result of rising levels of FSH and estrogen, the endometrial lining of the uterus begins to thicken, cervical mucus begins to thin, and oocytes mature within their follicles (fluid-filled sacs in the ovaries).

Ovulation

- The estrogen production stimulates levels of luteinizing hormone (LH) to surge at around day 14 of the cycle triggering one of the follicles to rupture and release the oocyte from the ovary to near a fallopian tube. This process is called **ovulation**. Once released, the oocyte is called an ovum. It can live for 24 hours. A female's level of testosterone peaks at ovulation in order to stimulate a woman's desire for sexual relations.

The Luteal Phase ("premenstrual phase")

- Lasts approximately 14 days after ovulation (until the final day of the cycle)
- The follicular cells that are left behind in the ovary become the **corpus luteum**.
- The corpus luteum secretes both estrogen and progesterone.
- Together they stimulate the endometrium to prepare a thick blanket of blood vessels and tissue that will support an embryo if fertilization should occur.
- If fertilization does occur, a signal is sent to maintain the corpus luteum which supports the embryo until a placenta is formed.

WORKSHEET #16 (CONTINUED)

Menstrual Phase

- If fertilization does not occur, the corpus luteum deteriorates, progesterone and estrogen levels fall, and the endometrium is shed during **the menstrual phase** (days 1 to 5).

- During the menstrual phase, estrogen and progesterone levels are low, which stimulates signals from the brain for FSH levels to begin to rise and begin the cycle once again.

1. *What is the average age of menarche (first menstrual cycle)?*

Between 11 + 13

2. *What stops menstrual blood from flowing?*

Constriction
of Arteries

3. *How much fluid is lost, on average, during menstruation?*

about 1
tablespoon

WORKSHEET #17

NAME _____

Vocabulary Challenge

Place the correct letter in the space on the left.

External Female Anatomy

_____1. Hymen

_____2. Vulva

_____3. Clitoral hood

_____4. Labia majora

A. Where the labia minora meets at the top

B. Tissue covering the entrance to the vagina

C. External female genitalia

D. The folds of fatty tissue that extend from the mons to the perineum

Internal Female Anatomy

_____1. Fallopian tube

_____2. Uterus

_____3. Vagina

_____4. Ovary

A. Fertilization occurs here

B. Birth canal

C. It produces estrogen

D. Houses the developing fetus

Breast and Gynecologic Disorders

_____1. Cyst

_____2. Fibroadenoma

_____3. Mammogram

_____4. Pap

A. Screening test for cervical cancer

B. A fluid-filled sac

C. Screening test for breast cancer

D. A solid, benign lump

PART II: READING

Female Genital Mutilation

PART I

Background Information

- Female genital mutilation (FGM) includes procedures that intentionally alter or cause injury to the female genital organs for nonmedical reasons.

- The procedure has no health benefits for girls and women.

- Procedures can cause severe bleeding and problems with urination, infections, and infertility as well as complications in childbirth including increased risk of newborn deaths.

- About 140 million girls and women worldwide are currently living with the consequences of FGM.

- FGM is mostly carried out on young girls sometime between infancy and age 15.

- In Africa an estimated 101 million girls 10 years old and above have undergone FGM. The practice is most common in the western, eastern, and northeastern regions of Africa, and some countries in Asia and the Middle East, and among migrants from these areas.

The practice is mostly carried out by traditional circumcisers, some of whom have no medical training and perform the procedure using unsterilized instruments and no anesthesia. However, more than 18% of all FGM is performed by healthcare providers, and this trend is increasing.

Female genital mutilation is typically performed in one of three ways:

1. *Clitoridectomy*: partial or total removal of the clitoris

2. *Excision*: partial or total removal of the clitoris and the labia minora, with or without excision of the labia majora

3. *Infibulation*: narrowing of the vaginal opening through the creation of a covering seal. The seal is formed by cutting and repositioning the inner or outer labia, with or without removal of the clitoris

FGM has no health benefits, and it harms girls and women in many ways. It involves removing and damaging healthy and normal female genital tissue, and interferes with the natural functions of girls' and women's bodies.

Immediate complications can include severe pain, shock, hemorrhage (bleeding), tetanus or sepsis (bacterial infection), urine retention, open sores in the genital region and injury to nearby genital tissue.

Long-term consequences can include:

- recurrent bladder and urinary tract infections
- cysts
- infertility
- an increased risk of childbirth complications and newborn deaths
- the need for later surgeries. For example, the FGM procedure that seals or narrows a vaginal opening (type 3 above) needs to be cut open later to allow for sexual intercourse and childbirth. Sometimes it is stitched again several times, including after childbirth, hence the woman goes through repeated opening and closing procedures, further increasing both immediate and long-term risks.

Procedures are mostly carried out on young girls sometime between infancy and age 15, and occasionally on adult women. In Africa, more than 3 million girls have been estimated to be at risk for FGM annually.

The causes of female genital mutilation include a mix of cultural and social factors within families and communities.

- FGM is often considered a necessary part of raising a girl properly, and a way to prepare her for adulthood and marriage.
- In some cultures, a woman is considered to be the property of her husband. The procedure provides the man with more assurance of marital fidelity. When a vaginal opening is covered or narrowed (type 3 above), the fear of the pain of opening it, and the fear that this will be found out, is expected to discourage "illicit" sexual intercourse among women with this type of FGM.
- Though no religious scripts recommend the practice, practitioners often believe the practice has religious support.
- Religious leaders take varying positions with regard to FGM: some promote it, some consider it irrelevant to religion, and others contribute to its elimination.
- While some groups and organizations strive to eliminate the practice of FGM, some community leaders, religious leaders, circumcisers, and even medical personnel contribute to upholding the practice.
- In most societies, FGM is considered a cultural tradition, which is often used as an argument for its continuation.

FGM is recognized internationally by the World Health Organization (WHO), the United Nations General Assembly, and others, as a violation of the human rights of girls and women. It reflects deep-rooted inequality between the sexes, and constitutes an extreme form of discrimination against women.

It is nearly always carried out on minors and is a violation of the rights of children. The practice also violates a person's rights to health and security, and the right to be free from torture and cruel, inhuman, or degrading treatment.

In 2010 WHO published a "global strategy to stop healthcare providers from performing female genital mutilation" in collaboration with other key UN agencies and international organizations.

WHO efforts to eliminate female genital mutilation focus on:

- *strengthening the response of healthcare professionals*: improving training and policy to ensure that health professionals can provide medical care and counseling to girls and women living with FGM
- *building evidence*: generating knowledge about the causes and consequences of the practice, how to eliminate it, and how to care for those with experienced FGM
- *increasing advocacy*: improving international, regional, and local efforts to end FGM within a generation

WHO is particularly concerned about the increasing trend for medically trained personnel to perform FGM, though WHO strongly urges health professionals not to perform such procedures.

In December 2012, the UN General Assembly accepted a resolution on the elimination of female genital mutilation.

PART II

The following are excerpts from the story that appeared in the New York Times in 2007:

KAFR AL MANSHI ABOU HAMAR, Egypt – The men in this poor farming community were furious. A 13-year-old girl was brought to a doctor's office to have her clitoris removed, a surgery considered necessary here to preserve chastity and honor.

The girl died, but that was not the source of the outrage. After her death, the government shut down the clinic, and that got everyone stirred up. "They will not stop us," shouted a tea shop owner along the main street. "We support circumcision!" he shouted over and over. "Even if the state doesn't like it, we will circumcise the girls," shouted an elder in the village.

Circumcision, as supporters call it, or *female genital mutilation*, as opponents refer to it, was suddenly a bitter focus of debate in Egypt in the summer of 2007. A nationwide campaign to stop the practice had become one of the most powerful social movements in Egypt in decades, uniting an unlikely alliance of government forces, official religious leaders, and street-level activists.

Though Egypt's Health Ministry ordered an end to the practice in 1996, it allowed exceptions in cases of emergency, a loophole critics described as so wide that it effectively rendered the ban meaningless. But now the government is trying to force a comprehensive ban.

Not only was it unusual for the government to shut down the clinic, but the health minister also issued a decree banning healthcare workers – or anyone – from conducting the procedure for any reason. Beyond that, the Ministry of Religious Affairs also issued a booklet explaining why the practice was not called for in Islam; Egypt's grand mufti, Ali Gomaa, declared it haram, or prohibited by Islam; Egypt's highest religious official, Muhammed Sayyid Tantawi, called it harmful; television advertisements have been shown on state channels to discourage it; and a national hotline was set up to answer the public's questions about genital cutting.

Although the men in this village demonstrated, widespread social change in Egypt, or anywhere else, comes very slowly.

For centuries Egyptian girls, usually between the ages of 7 and 13, have been taken to have the procedure done, sometimes by a doctor, sometimes by a barber or whoever else in the village would do it. As recently as 2005, a government health survey showed that 96% of the thousands of married, divorced, and widowed women interviewed said they had undergone the procedure – a figure that astounds even many Egyptians. In the language of the survey, "the practice of female circumcision is virtually universal among women of reproductive age in Egypt."

For the last several years, forces opposing genital cutting in Egypt are speaking out as never before. More than a century after the first efforts to curb this custom, the movement has broken through one of the main barriers to change: it is no longer considered taboo to discuss in public. That shift seems to have coincided with a small but growing acceptance of talking about human sexuality on television and radio.

The force behind this unlikely collaboration between government, nongovernment organizations, religious leaders and the news media is a no-nonsense 84-year-old activist named Marie Assaad, who has been fighting against genital cutting for decades.

Dr. Nasr el-Sayyid, assistant to the minister of health, said there had already been a drop in urban areas, along with an aggressive effort in more than 100 villages, mostly in the south, to curb the practice. "Our plan and program over the next two years is aiming to take it down 20% nationwide," he said.

The challenge, however, rests in convincing people that their grandparents, parents and they themselves have harmed their daughters. Moreover, advocates must convince the public that an Egyptian man will marry a woman who has not undergone the procedure and that circumcision is not necessary to preserve family honor. It is a challenge to get men to give up some of their control over women.

And it will be a challenge to convince influential people like Osama Mohammed el-Moaseri, Imam of a mosque in Basyoun, the city near where the 13-year-old girl lived, and died. "This practice has been passed down generation after generation, so it is natural that every person circumcise his daughter," he said. "When Ali Gomaa says it is haram, he is criticizing the practice of our fathers and forefathers."

NAME _____

We have an obligation, on the basis of human rights, to support the elimination of the practice of FGM.

or

We must respect the rights of people in other cultures to practice whatever traditions they wish.

Which statement best sums up your feelings? Explain.

_____

_____

_____

_____

_____

_____

_____

_____

_____

_____

_____

_____

_____

_____

_____

_____

_____

_____

REFERENCES

Centers for Disease Control and Prevention. *Breast Cancer:Risk Factors.* Updated Jan. 10, 2013. Web. 9 Feb. 2013. <http://www.cdc.gov/cancer/breast/basic_info/risk_factors.htm>

Centers for Disease Control and Prevention. *Gynecologic Cancers: Basic Information About Gynecologic Cancers.* Updated Dec. 9, 2010. Web. 9 Feb. 2013. <http://www.cdc.gov/cancer/gynecologic/basic_info/index.htm>

National Cancer Institute. *BRCA1 and BRCA2: Cancer Risk & Genetic Testing.* Last reviewed May 29, 2009. *NCI.* Web. 11 Aug. 2013. <http://www.cancer.gov/cancertopics/factsheet/Risk/BRCA>

World Health Organization (2008). *Eliminating Female Genital Mutilation: An Interagency Statement.* Web. 3 Feb. 2013. <www.who.int/reproductivehealth/publications/fgm/9789241596442/en/index.html>

PART III

MALE REPRODUCTIVE ANATOMY AND PHYSIOLOGY

WORKSHEET #18

External Male Anatomy

The Penis

The penis has three functions:

1. It is the passageway through which urine leaves the body.

2. It is the passageway through which sperm leaves the body.

3. It is the primary organ of sexual pleasure in males.

The penis has three sections: the glans, the shaft, and the root. The human penis does not contain a bone and has little muscle. It is made up of nerves, blood vessels, and three cylinders of spongy tissue that fill with blood to cause erection.

Components of the Penis

The **glans**, or head, is often the most sensitive part of the penis. It is set apart from the shaft by the raised edge called the **corona**. On the glans is an opening called the **meatus**, through which urine or semen are expelled. On the underside of the penis is a thin strip of flesh called the **frenulum** which connects the shaft to the head.

When the penis is flaccid (not erect), the glans is at least partially covered with a loose fold of skin called **foreskin**, except when the skin has been removed by circumcision. The foreskin has protective and sensory functions. It protects the glans from trauma. It also contains many sensory receptors, making the foreskin one of the most sensitive areas of the penis. Beneath the foreskin are a number of small glands that produce a waxy substance that lubricates the foreskin. If this fluid accumulates, it combines with dead skin and bacteria to become **smegma**, a thick and foul-smelling substance that can lead to discomfort and infection if not properly cleaned.

The **shaft**, or body of the penis, consists of the three cylinders of spongy tissue that will fill with blood during sexual arousal. The **root** of the penis enters the body just below the pubic bone and is attached to internal pelvic muscles. The root of the penis goes farther into the body than most people realize; can be felt in the perineum (the area of skin between the scrotum and anus), particularly when the penis is erect.

WORKSHEET #18 (CONTINUED)

Erection

✳Erections can occur with any form of stimulation the individual perceives as sexual – sights, sounds, smells, or thoughts for example. In addition, involuntary erections occur during sleep several times each night in healthy men. During an erection, nerve fibers cause the arteries of the penis to dilate, allowing blood to rush into the spongy tissues in the shaft (known as the corpora cavernosa and corpus spongiosum), while veins constrict to prevent blood from escaping. The rush of blood into the tissues causes the penis to become erect.

The penis returns to its flaccid state when the arteries constrict and the blood is able to drain out through the veins.

In addition to the cardiovascular component, erection is basically a spinal reflex. Depending on the location of the injury, men who have spinal cord injuries can sometimes achieve reflex erections in which their penis becomes erect even though they feel no sensation.

The Scrotum

✳The scrotum is a loose pouch beneath the penis, covered with sparse pubic hair. The scrotum contains the testicles, each in a sac, separated by a thin layer of tissue. The testicles sit outside the body. This is because the production and survival of sperm require a temperature that is four degrees lower than the body's temperature. When the testicles become too hot, such as following immersion in a hot tub, sperm production is inhibited.

The scrotum can rise or fall depending on temperature and sexual activity. The scrotum is able to regulate testicular temperature using two mechanisms. First, the skin of the scrotum contains many sweat glands which cool the testicles when they become too warm. Second, the cremaster muscle of the scrotum contracts and expands. When the testicles become too cool, they are drawn closer to the body to increase their temperature; when they become too warm, they are lowered away from the body to reduce their temperature. Men often experience the phenomenon of having the scrotum relax and hang low when taking a warm shower, only to tighten up when cold air hits it after exiting the shower.

The scrotum also contracts and elevates the testicles in response to sexual arousal, which may be to protect the testicles from injury during sexual behavior.

WORKSHEET #19

The Testicles and Sperm Production

The Testicles

The testicles (also referred to as the testes) are egg-shaped glands that rest in the scrotum, each about two inches long and one inch diameter. The left testicle usually hangs lower than right in most men, although this can be reversed in left-handed men. Having one testicle lower than the other helps one slide over the other instead of crushing together when compressed. The testicles serve two main functions: spermatogenesis (the production of sperm) and testosterone production.

The Process of Sperm Production

1. Sperm production begins at puberty and usually continues throughout a man's life.

2. Sperm production begins in approximately 300 microscopic tubes located in the testes, known as __seminiferous tubules__. In human males, sperm formation requires approximately 72 days. Because sperm is constantly being produced, males produce about 300 million sperm per day.

3. Once formed, immature sperm migrate to the *epididymis* where they mature for about 10 to 14 days and where some abnormal or old sperm are reabsorbed. The epididymis is a snail-like organ that sits at the top of each testicle and can be easily felt if the testicle is gently rolled between the fingers. After sperm have matured, the epididymis pushes them into the vas deferens, where they can be stored for several months.

4. The *vas deferens* carry mature sperm from each epididymis to the *ejaculatory ducts*. Each vas deferens is about 18 inches long. The end of each of these tubes widens into an ampulla, which is a sac-like swelling in which sperm may be stored for varying periods of time. A *vasectomy* is a procedure in which the vas are severed, preventing sperm from reaching the ejaculatory ducts.

5. From the vas deferens, the ejaculate passes on to the ejaculatory ducts, which are two short (about one inch) tubes that pass through the prostate gland, terminating at the urethra.

6. The *urethra*, the tube of smooth muscle that runs the length of the penis, carries both sperm and urine to the outside world.

7. *Seminal vesicles (glands)*

Only about one percent of the fluid that is ejaculated from the penis is sperm. The rest is *seminal fluid.* Seminal fluid comes from three glands: the seminal vesicles, the prostate gland, and Cowper's glands. Seminal fluid contains water, enzymes, vitamins, minerals, fructose, and other substances. Its purpose is to provide nutrition and protection for the sperm during their journey through the female reproductive tract. A man typically ejaculates about one to two teaspoons of semen (containing about 300 million sperm), although this can decrease with age and frequency of ejaculation.

About two thirds of the total volume of seminal fluid is produced by the two *seminal vesicles*. These are pouchlike glands, about two inches long, located behind the bladder, that empty into the ejaculatory duct.

8. *Prostate gland*

The *prostate gland* is a doughnut-shaped gland, about the size of a walnut, that encircles the urethra. The prostate contributes about 30% of the total seminal fluid. The milky, alkaline secretions of the prostate contain enzymes, proteins, and minerals to enhance motility and survival of the sperm.

9. *Cowper's glands*

Cowper's glands are two pea-sized glands that lie below the prostate. They secrete a small amount of clear alkaline fluid, to lubricate the urethra. Pre-ejaculatory fluid comes from the Cowper's glands. Pre-ejaculatory fluid *can* contain sperm. If the man has recently ejaculated, sperm may survive in the urethra and be carried out in the pre-ejaculatory fluid.

Testosterone

Testosterone is one of a number of *androgens,* hormones that produce male *secondary sexual characteristics* such as body and facial hair, and a deep voice. Both males and females have testosterone, although males make ten times more of it than females. Males produce most of their testosterone in the testes. A small amount is produced by the *adrenal glands*. This hormone is necessary for the production of sperm, and plays a role in sexual desire and activity. It increases aggression animals, although the question of whether testosterone also increases human aggression is controversial.

Male Reproductive System (Side View)

Underlined not on exam

* On test

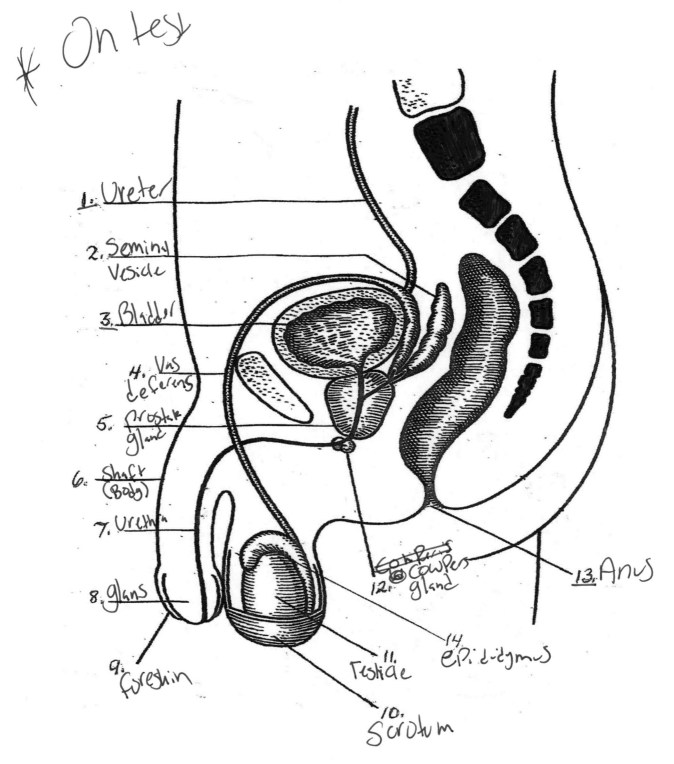

1. Ureter
2. Seminal Vesicle
3. Bladder
4. Vas deferens
5. Prostate gland
6. Shaft (Body)
7. Urethra
8. Glans
9. Foreskin
10. Scrotum
11. Testicle
12. Cowpers gland
13. Anus
14. Epididymus

WORKSHEET #21

Male Circumcision

Male circumcision, surgical removal of the foreskin of the penis, is one of the most commonly performed surgical procedures in the United States, although the rate seems to be falling (Rabin, 2010). Circumcision is most often performed for religious tradition or personal preference.

Male Circumcision: Medical Pros and Cons

Benefits of male circumcision include:

- Circumcision may result in a decreased incidence of *urinary tract infections*.
- Circumcision may result in a lower incidence of *sexually transmitted diseases* and may reduce *HIV* transmission.
- Circumcision may lower the risk for *cancer* of the cervix in *sexual partners*.
- Circumcision may decrease the risk for *cancer of the penis*.
- Circumcised males cannot develop *phimosis* (a tight, nonretractable foreskin).

Risks of male circumcision include:

- Pain
- Risk of bleeding and infection at the site of the circumcision
- Irritation of the glans
- Increased risk of meatitis (inflammation of the opening of the penis)
- Risk of injury to the penis

After a comprehensive review of scientific evidence, the American Academy of Pediatrics found the health benefits of newborn male circumcision outweigh the risks, but the benefits are not great enough to recommend universal newborn circumcision. The AAP policy statement published Monday, August 27, 2012 says the final decision should still be left to parents to make in the context of their religious, ethical, and cultural beliefs (American Academy of Pediatrics, 2012).

WORKSHEET #22

Male Puberty and Male Andropause

Male Puberty

At an average of ten years of age, the hypothalamus begins releasing gonadotropin- releasing hormone (GnRH), which stimulates the anterior pituitary gland to send out follicle-stimulating hormone (FSH) and luteinizing hormone. These hormones flow through the circulatory system to the testes, where LH stimulates the production of the male sex hormone, testosterone, which, together with LH, stimulates sperm production.

As puberty progresses, the testicles grow, and the penis begins to grow about a year later. The epididymis, prostate, seminal vesicles, and Cowper's glands also grow over the next several years. Increased testosterone stimulates an overall growth spurt in puberty, as bones and muscles rapidly develop. This spurt can be dramatic; teenage boys can grow three or four inches within a few months. The elevation of testosterone affects a number of male traits: the boy develops longer and heavier bones, larger muscles, thicker and tougher skin, a deepening voice because of growth of the voice box, pubic hair, facial and chest hair, increased sex drive, and increased metabolism.

Sperm production begins at about 12 years of age. The ejaculation of mature sperm usually does not occur for about another one to one and a half years. At puberty, FSH begins to stimulate sperm production in the seminiferous tubules, and the increased testosterone induces the testes to mature fully. The development of sperm and the seminal vesicles and prostate gland allows the boy to begin to experience his first nocturnal emissions, although at the beginning, they tend to contain a very low live sperm count.

Male Andropause

Men do not go through obvious stages as menopausal women do, but some experience a less well-defined set of symptoms. Although a man's ability to ejaculate healthy sperm may be retained throughout his life, sperm production does decrease with age. The ejaculate becomes thinner and ejaculatory pressure decreases.

With age, a man's blood testosterone concentration decreases. The reduction in testosterone production results in decreased muscle strength, decreased libido, easy fatigue, and mood fluctuations.

The use of androgen (testosterone) replacement therapy is somewhat controversial because of the possibility of an increased risk for prostate cancer, but current research does not support this risk. Consequently, the use of androgen replacement therapy is commonly used in the U.S. today (Bassil & Morley, 2010).

WORKSHEET #23

Disorders of the Male Reproductive System

Testicular Cancer

While testicular cancer is a relatively rare form of cancer, accounting for only about one percent of new cancers in men, it is the most common malignancy in men between the ages of 25 to 34.

The first sign of testicular cancer is usually a slight enlargement in one of the testicles, which can be detected by self-examination. The man may also feel a dull ache in the lower abdomen or heaviness in his testicles. There are few symptoms until the cancer is advanced, which is why early detection is so important.

White men get testicular cancer four to five times more frequently than African-American men. Within the given race, men in higher socioeconomic groups are twice as likely to be diagnosed with testicular cancer compared with those in lower socioeconomic groups.

Risk factors for testicular cancer include a family history and cryptorchidism (undescended testicles). Newer research has found that smoking cigarettes or marijuana may increase a man's risk of testicular cancer. There is also a higher incidence among brothers of men with testicular cancer, suggesting a genetic predisposition (Neale, Carrière, Murphy, & Baade, 2008).

The survival rate is almost 90%. This is primarily due to early detection. Although the incidence of testicular cancer has continuously increased during the last few decades, cure rates have significantly improved. Treatment may involve radiation, chemotherapy, or the removal of the testicle (although radiation and chemotherapy can affect future fertility, the removal of the testicle does not). If removal of the testicle is necessary, some men opt to get a prosthetic testicle implanted, which gives the appearance of having two testicles.

Testicular self-examination should be done once a month.

It is best to check your testicles after a warm bath or shower. First, visually inspect your testicles in front of a mirror to see any signs of swelling. Then support your testicles with one hand and feel each testis with the other hand. Slowly roll each testis between your thumb and the first two fingers of one hand. Testicles normally feel smooth and slightly spongy. See your doctor if you feel any swelling, unusual firmness, tenderness, or lumps.

Penile Cancer

The main symptom of penile cancer is a sore, irritation, or lump on the penis. Any lesion on the penis must be examined by a physician since noncancerous lesions, STI's, and malignancies can all look very similar.

The risk for penile cancer is increased in men over the age of 60, in those who are uncircumcised, and in those who smoke. The American Cancer Society estimates that in the U.S. in 2013, 1,570 new cases of penile cancer will be diagnosed and about 310 men will die from it (American Cancer Society, 2013).

Prostate Cancer

Prostate cancer is the second leading cause of cancer-related death in American men, behind only lung cancer. Skin cancers non-withstanding, it is the most commonly diagnosed cancer in men. Usually found in men over the age of 65, 8 to 12% of the population will develop prostate cancer. Prostate cancer occurs almost 70% more often in African-American men than it does in white men in the U.S. and African-American men are more likely to die from it.

Several risk factors have been linked to prostate cancer. Men with a father or brother with prostate cancer are two to three times as more likely to develop prostate cancer. Other risk factors include race, age, and a diet high in fat. Studies have shown that men whose diets include high levels of red and processed meats have higher risks. On the other hand, broccoli, tomatoes, and pomegranate juice may help to lower the risk.

Early signs of prostate cancer may include lower back or pelvic pain; inability to urinate; loss of force in the urinary stream; pain or burning during urination; or blood in the urine.

Prostate cancer is detected most commonly by a digital rectal exam, in which the doctor inserts a finger in the rectum to feel for lumps or hardening and by a blood test measuring levels of prostate specific antigen (PSA), a protein made in the prostate. The American Cancer Society recommends yearly screening for prostate cancer beginning at 50 years of age (although those at risk are advised to begin screening sooner).

WORKSHEET #24

Questions Regarding Male Reproductive Anatomy and Physiology

1. *What is cryptorchidism and how is it treated?*

2. *If a couple is trying to conceive a baby, it's probably not a good idea for the pair to spend lots of time in a hot tub. Why*

3. *What is artificial insemination?*

WORKSHEET #25

NAME _____

Vocabulary Challenge

Place the correct letter in the space on the left.

The Penis

_____1. Root

_____2. Shaft

_____3. Meatus

_____4. Foreskin

A. Partially covers the glans

B. Opening on the glans

C. Attached to internal pelvic muscles

D. Body of the penis

Testicles & Sperm Production

_____1. Cowper's Glands

_____2. Epididymus

_____3. Prostate Gland

_____4. Vas Deference

A. Where sperm mature

B. Tubes which are about 18 inches long

C. Pre-ejaculatory fluid

D. 30% of the total volume of seminal fluid comes from here

Disorders Involving the Male Reproductive System

_____1. Cryptorchism

_____2. Prostate Cancer

_____3. Penile Cancer

_____4. Testicular Cancer

A. Most common malignancy in men aged 25 to 34

B. Increased risk in uncircumcised men

C. Detected with a PSA blood test

D. Undescended testicles

PART III: READING

Testicular Cancer: A Personal Story

In June of 2003, Today Show legal analyst, Dan Abrams, noticed that his right testicle felt swollen. On a friend's recommendation, the 34-year-old lawyer and television personality saw a doctor to check it out. The doctor said that he strongly suspected testicular cancer and ordered an ultrasound and CAT scan that very day. Once the diagnosis was confirmed, Abrams saw a cancer specialist at Memorial Sloan-Kettering Cancer Center in New York City. He was feeling stunned and freaked out, but knew that he had to focus on what to do next.

On July 7th, in a 45 minute surgery, a surgeon at Memorial Sloan Kettering Cancer Center removed Abrams' right testicle, thus removing the cancer.

He had two CAT scans, both clean, which meant that the cancer hadn't visibly spread. But they performed a biopsy, and two days later, with his parents in the doctor's office, the doctor told Abrams the tumor had gotten into blood vessels around the testicle. He remembered thinking, "Come on, give me a break. That conversation made me realize that I wasn't going to automatically put this behind me. Now, I was really worried."

The doctor told him there was a 50% chance the disease had already spread to his lymph nodes and beyond. Now, he had a choice: wait and hope that it hadn't spread or take action and have what's called a retroperitoneal lymph node dissection. That procedure involves removing all the lymph nodes in the abdomen. It would not only tell for certain if the cancer had spread but could also remove it if it had spread. He decided on surgery.

Cutting just below the breast bone all the way to the pelvis, the doctor removed 59 lymph nodes in six hours. The lymph nodes still had to be biopsied and as it turned out, they were free of cancer. He didn't have to go through chemo. On the fifth day after surgery, he was discharged from the hospital.

Still, the surgery was tough. For weeks he needed help getting out of bed or off the couch and walked with a cane. He lost 25 pounds.

Today, he feels really lucky. His parents and friends helped him and then there was his girlfriend. They started seeing each other months into recovery, and she was incredibly supportive. Today, he's looking forward to the life he had always envisioned – career, kids, everything. "These days, probably because of my job I think more about terror attacks in New York City than I do about dying from cancer." Now that he's talked about it publicly, people come up to him on the street and say, "Hey, I'm glad you're okay." He'd probably prefer that they say, "Hey, you're the guy on that news show." "But," he said, "if it means that they're going to do a self-check for testicular cancer, and maybe tell someone they love about it too, then it was worth it."

NAME _____

1. *Why do so many young men wait before seeing a doctor about a lump or pain in a testicle?*

2. *What steps can be taken to make males more aware of testicular cancer and the importance of early detection?*

_____

_____

_____

_____

_____

_____

_____

_____

_____

_____

_____

_____

_____

_____

_____

_____

_____

_____

_____

_____

REFERENCES

American Academy of Pediatrics. *Newborn Male Circumcision*. Oct. 27, 2012. *AAP.* Web. 12 Feb. 2013. <http://www.aap.org/en-us/about-the-aap-press-room/Pages/Newborn-Male-Circumcision.aspx>

American Cancer Society. *What Are the Key Statistics about Testicular Cancer?* Last revised Jan. 17, 2013. *ACS.* Web. 15 Feb. 2013. <http://www.cancer.org/cancer/testicularcancer/detailedguide/testicular-cancer-key-statistics>

Bassil, N. and Morley, J.E. (2010). Late-life onset hypergonadism: a review. *Clinical Geriatric Medicine*, 26 (2), 197-222.

Makrantonaki, E., Schönknecht, P., Hossini, A. M., Kaiser, E., Katsouli, M.M., Addjaye, J., Schröder, J., and Zouboulis, C.C. (2010). Skin and brain age together: the role of hormones in the aging process. *Experimental Gerontology*, 45(10), 801-813.

Neale, R.E., Carrière, P., Murphy, M.F.G., and Baade, P.D. (2008). Testicular cancer in twins: a meta-analysis. *British Journal of Cancer*, 98(1), 171-173.

Rabin, R.C. (2010). *Steep Drop Seen in Circumcision in U.S.* New York Times. Web. 17 Feb. 2013. <http://www.nytimes.com/2010/08/17/health/research/17circ.html?_r=1.>

PART IV

SEXUALITY DURING CHILDHOOD, ADOLESCENCE, AND THE ADULT YEARS

WORKSHEET #26

Sexuality in Childhood and Adolescence

Children show a broad range of sexual behaviors.

Early childhood (ages 2 to 5)

Toddlers and young children engage in many behaviors that involve exploration of their own bodies.

- Genital touching is more common in early childhood than in later childhood, and it picks up again after puberty.

- Not only are children curious about their own bodies, but beginning at about the age of three, they become very interested in other people's bodies as well.

- Their natural curiosity leads them to want to see other children naked and engage in games involving exposing the genitals.

Middle childhood to preteen (ages 6 to 12)

- Children begin building a knowledge base about sexual information. They often acquire information from many sources, including parents, siblings, friends, and the media.

- Both boys and girls become more private about their bodies.

- By the time children are 8 to 9 years of age the tendency is for boys and girls to play separately.

- Although romantic interest in the other sex may exist, there is a decline in sex play with others.

- Most 10 to 11 year olds become very self-conscious about their bodies.

Adolescence (ages 13 to 18)

- Although the age at which puberty normally begins varies greatly, the signs typically unfold between the ages of 11 and 16 for boys and 8 and 16 for girls.

- The importance of friends grows and many adolescents rate their friends as their most important relationships.

- Young adolescents are often preoccupied with body image.

- Many adolescents become increasingly interested in forming intimate relationships and gay and lesbian youth often feel intense pressure to express interest in male-female relationships.

WORKSHEET #27

Puberty

Puberty is the time of life when an individual becomes capable of reproduction.

The brain coordinates the physical changes that occur during puberty. The process begins when the hypothalamus causes the pituitary gland to release increased amounts of hormones, known as gonadotropins, into the bloodstream. These hormones stimulate activity in the testes in males and the ovaries in females. In males, they cause the testes to increase testosterone production and in females, the hormones act on the ovaries to increase the production of estrogen. In response to an increase in either testosterone or estrogen, signs of male and female sexual maturation appear.

Female Puberty

The proportion of girls who experience the physical changes of puberty as early as ages seven and eight is increasing. While more research is needed to explain the connections, diet, obesity, and exposure to environmental pollutants may be contributing to this trend.

The physical changes that accompany puberty in females include:

- Maturation and growth in size of the vagina, uterus, and fallopian tubes
- Breast development
- Broadening of the pelvis
- Development of pubic and axillary hair

Usually at the age of 11 or 12, females will begin to ovulate. The beginning of ovulation corresponds to menarche, the first menstrual period. However, some females may begin menstruating a few months before their first ovulation, while others may ovulate a few times before their first full menstrual cycle. The average age of menarche in the U.S. is 12 to 13 years, but that number has been gradually decreasing. In less developed countries, the age of menarche is later. Various environmental factors, such as poor nutrition, can delay menarche. Also, heredity plays a role. Girls experience menarche at about the same age as their mothers.

WORKSHEET #27 (CONTINUED)

Male Puberty

The two major functions of the testes – to produce male hormones and to produce sperm – are dormant in young boys. Then at an average of 10 years of age, the hypothalamus stimulates the pituitary gland to release follicle-stimulating hormone (FSH) and luteinizing hormone (LH) (the same hormones that are released during puberty in young girls).

These hormones flow through the circulatory system to the testes where the LH stimulates the production of the male sex hormone, testosterone. Testosterone, together with LH, stimulate sperm production

As the process of puberty progresses, the testicles grow – as does the penis beginning about a year later. The epididymis, prostate, seminal vesicles, and Cowper's glands also grow over the next few years.

The increased level of testosterone during puberty stimulates a growth spurt in males, which corresponds with rapid bone and muscle development. The growth spurt can be quite dramatic – some boys grow 3 to 4 inches within a few months.

Other physical changes that accompany puberty in males include:

- A deepening of the voice (because of growth and thickening of the larynx)
- Thicker skin
- Facial, chest, pubic, and axillary hair

While sperm production begins at about 12 years of age, the ejaculation of mature sperm usually doesn't occur for another 12 to 18 months. Though boys may experience ejaculations through, for example, nocturnal emissions – initially the ejaculations contain a very low sperm count.

WORKSHEET #28

The Beginnings of Sexual Activity

The most characteristic sexual behavior of adolescents is not partnered sexual behavior, such as intercourse, but masturbation (Fortenberry et al., 2010).

National surveys show a strong upper trend in adolescent sexual intercourse from the 1950s through the 1980s (see table below). The results of more recent surveys reveal that the upward trend leveled off and then decreased somewhat over the next two decades. More recently, rates have increased slightly (Eaton et al., 2010).

The rates of intercourse in teens is very age-dependent: while 53 to 66% of 18 to 19 year olds have had sex, only 30 to 33% of 16 to 17 year olds and about 10% of 14 to 15 year olds have had vaginal intercourse (Fortenberry et al., 2010).

Percentage of Adolescents Who Reported
Experiencing Coitus by Age 19

Study	Females (%)	Males (%)
Kinsey et al. (1948, 1953)	20	45
Zelnick & Kantner (1980)	69	77
Centers for Disease Control (1996)	66	67
Centers for Disease Control (2006A)	62	64

As the rates of vaginal intercourse have basically leveled off, more adolescents are having oral sex. Forty-seven percent of 15 to 19 year olds have had oral sex with someone of the opposite sex (Chandra et al., 2011). In a survey of ninth graders, almost 20% has had oral sex (Halpern-Felsher, Cornell, Kropp, & Tschann, 2005).

Fortunately, adolescents are increasingly likely to use contraception (Eaton et al., 2010). Fortenberry and colleagues (2010) reported that in 1991, 46% of students reported using a condom the last time they had intercourse; in 2009, the number increased to 61%; and by 2010, 80% of males reported using a condom during the last time they had intercourse.

Thought Provoking Question:

A significant percentage of young people are engaging in sexual activity (oral sex, anal sex, vaginal sex) in their mid-teens or even early adolescence.   Do you believe that this is a good time to begin sexual activity or do you think that it is too soon?   What do you think is the ideal age to begin experimenting with sex? What factors influence your opinion?

_____

_____

_____

_____

_____

_____

_____

_____

_____

_____

_____

_____

_____

_____

WORKSHEET #29

Cohabitation

Cohabitation - living together and having an emotionally and physically intimate relationship without being married

The number of cohabitating couples has increased significantly over the last few years. While there were 3.2 million unmarried couples living together in 1990, the number grew to 7.5 million couples in 2010. Forty-four percent of all adults in the United States have cohabitated at some point in their lives (Pew Research Center, 2010).

There is no evidence that living together before marriage strengthens the marriage. In fact, couples who are committed to each other (i.e. planning to marry) have the same chance of divorce as couples who marry without living together first (Goodwin et al., 2010.)

- *What are your thoughts about cohabitating?*
- *What are important topics to discuss with your partner before moving in together?*

WORKSHEET #30

Dating Violence among College Students (IPV – Intimate Partner Violence)

Studies suggest that between 20% and 47% of men and women are victims of physical dating violence in their relationships (Kaura & Lohman, 2007). Psychological victimization is more prevalent than physical or sexual victimization and is not limited to relationships that are physically aggressive (Lawrence, BaYoon, MaLanger, & MaRo, 2009). One study (Katz, Arias, and Beach, 2000) found that 90% of college women reported psychological victimization at some point in their relationships. Despite strong evidence that males and females engage in similar numbers of nonsexual violence against intimate partners, female victims of IPV have repeatedly shown to be at greater risk than male victims for sustaining physical and psychological injury. The outcome of IPV for females in early adulthood can be fatal, with women between the ages of 20 and 29 having the greatest risk of being murdered by an intimate partner (Cercone, Beach, & Arias, 2005).

Risk Factors for College Student Dating Violence

1.	**Family history**	Observing violence between one's parents or caregivers; having a personal history of child abuse
2.	**Peer influences**	Individuals who overestimated or underestimated social standing with their peer group; hostile attitudes and acceptance of violence against women
3.	**Personal attitudes, beliefs and perceptions**	Research (West & Wandrei, 2002) indicates that male students, as compared to female students, are somewhat more likely to hold general violence-condoning, victim-blaming attitudes.
4.	**Alcohol use and abuse**	Alcohol is involved in the majority of cases of dating violence.
5.	**Psychological and emotional factors**	Factors such as low self-esteem, anti-social behavior, high levels of jealousy, and angry temperament have all been shown to relate significantly to college dating violence.

What steps can be taken to address the problem of dating violence among college students?

Women get more Physical injurys + Death than Men do when abused

WORKSHEET #31

Marriage

The proportion of married people 19 years of age and older decreased from 57% in 2000 to 52% in 2009, which is the lowest recorded percentage since the Census Bureau began collecting data. In fact, in 2009 the number of unmarried women (single, separated, divorced, or widowed) outnumbered the number of married women for the first time in U.S. history. Still, however, most people will get married at some point in their lives (Mather & Lauery, 2010).

1. Americans entering adulthood today face a much wider range of lifestyle choices than those available to earlier generations. Despite the fact that marriage remains the most common lifestyle in the United States, alternatives such as remaining single or cohabitating are choices being made by an increasing number of individuals and couples.

   Robert and Debbie are in a committed relationship. They have been living together for a year. They feel that they want to be together for the rest of their lives, but they're not sure whether or not to get married.

   What are the benefits that marriage brings? What are the drawbacks?

2. Some couples implement financial plans which they agree on before they are married (prenuptial agreements). Should the couples divorce, the terms agreed upon as the prenuptial agreement are implemented.

   Would you enter into a prenuptial agreement?

WORKSHEET #32

Divorce

At one time, a spouse seeking a divorce had to plead causes, such as adultery or cruelty. In the 1960s a movement to reform divorce laws began. By the 1990s, all 50 states had adopted "no-fault" divorces, in which both spouses agreed that the ending of the marriage is due to "irreconcilable differences" and do not legally blame the other for the breakdown of the marriage.

It is estimated that about one in five adults has divorced. The U.S. Census Bureau reports that 50% of U.S. marriages end in divorce (U.S. Census Bureau, 2007). The changes in divorce law have made it easier for couples to divorce. Divorce has also become much less stigmatized than in the past.

Economic changes also seem to have contributed to the rise in divorce rates. Divorce is more common when both partners are financially independent, and less common when spouses are dependent on each other to make ends meet or when one spouse is financially dependent on the other.

Still, these changes do not completely answer the question – Why do people get divorced?

Factors that may contribute to divorce include:
1. marrying because of an unplanned pregnancy
2. financial problems
3. sexual problems
4. alcohol or drug abuse
5. physical or emotional abuse
6. boredom/growing apart
7. extramarital sex
   Extramarital sex (also known as adultery, infidelity, or cheating) refers to sex outside of marriage.

If you felt that you and your spouse weren't feeling the same spark that you once felt in your relationship, what steps might you take to bring it back?

WORKSHEET #32 (CONTINUED)

It is difficult to accurately determine the incidence of infidelity. Studies suggest that approximately 1/3 of men and 1/4 of women engage in an extramarital sexual relationship at least once in their lives. When extramarital activities other than intercourse (such as kissing or emotional connections) are included, women report as many acts of infidelity as men (Mark, Janssen, & Milhausen, 2011).

Why do people cheat?

Boredem, Unmet needs, lust, revenge

Regardless of why it occurs, extramarital sex can have a destructive effect on the relationship. Couples therapists consider extramarital affairs to be one of the most damaging events to a relationship (Whisman & Snyder, 2007).

- *In a monogamous relationship, must intercourse occur for cheating to have taken place?*
- *What factors determine whether or not a marriage can remain intact after one has cheated on their partner?*

WORKSHEET #33

NAME _____

Puzzle Fill-In

WORKSHEET #33 (CONTINUED)

DOWN

1. Sperm production begins at about _____ years of age

2. During puberty, the _____ increase testosterone production

3. Though rates of vaginal intercourse are leveling off, more adolescents are having _____ sex

4. It's estimated that about one in _____ adults has divorced

5. In _____ divorces, neither spouse legally blames the other for the breakdown of the marriage

ACROSS

6. _____ percent of U.S. marriages end in divorce

7. During puberty, ovaries increase the production of _____

8. _____ is involved in the majority of dating violence cases

9. Male students are more likely than female students to hold _____ blaming attitudes

10. The number of cohabiting couples has _____ over the last few years

Heather Has Two Mommies

Heather Has Two Mommies is a children's book first published in 1989. The story is about a child, Heather, raised by a lesbian couple. The plot is that Heather goes to school and discovers that many of her schoolmates have families that look different from the one in which she's familiar. At Heather's playgroup, her family situation is discussed simply and positively, as are those of other children in nontraditional family units.

According to the book's author, Lesléa Newman, "The idea for Heather came about one day when I was walking down Main Street in Northampton, Massachusetts, a town known for its liberalism, tolerance of difference, and large gay and lesbian population. On this particular day I ran into a woman who, along with her female partner, had recently welcomed a child into their home." "We have no books to read to our daughter that show our type of family," the woman said. "Somebody should write one."

Heather Has Two Mommies caused an enormous amount of controversy in schools and communities around the country. The American Library Association ranked it the 11th most frequently challenged book in the United States in the 1990s. The controversy reignited the "banned books" debate. Books like *Huckleberry Finn* have been banned for containing the "N-word."

The "book banning" advocates argue that allowing a book such as *Heather Has Two Mommies* to be read in elementary schools is allowing schools to force their social views on children – undermining the right of parents. Those in favor of allowing the book to be used in schools cited concerns about censorship and asked, "How can it be wrong to encourage children to be tolerant of people different from themselves?"

NAME _____

No books are banned from being printed in the United States, however choices are made in the selection of books in our schools.

If you had been a parent of an elementary school child in 1989 and you were asked to permit "Heather Has Two Mommies" to be included among the books chosen by the district, how would you have responded? Explain.

_____

_____

_____

_____

_____

_____

_____

_____

_____

_____

_____

_____

_____

_____

_____

_____

_____

_____

_____

REFERENCES

Centers for Disease Control (1996). Youth risk behavior surveillance: United States, 1995. *Morbidity & Mortality Weekly Report*, 45 (SS-4), 1-84.

Centers for Disease Control (2006A). Youth risk behavior surveillance: United States, 2005. *Morbidity & Mortality Weekly Report*, 55, 1-108.

Cercone, J., Beach, S., and Arias, I. (2005). Gender symmetry in dating intimate partner violence: does similar behavior imply similar constructs? *Violence & Victims*, 20 (2), 207-208.

Chandra, A., Mosher, W.D., Copen, C., and Sionean, C. (2011). Sexual behavior, sexual attraction, and sexual identity in the United States: data from the 2006-2008 National Survey of Family Growth. National Health Statistics Report, 36, Hyattsville, MD: National Center for Health Statistics.

Eaton, D.K., Kann, L., Kinchen, S., Shanklin, S., Ross, J., Hawkins, J....Centers for Disease Control and Prevention. (2010, June 4). Youth risk behavior surveillance United States, 2009. in Surveillance Summaries (MMWR, 59 ([SS-5]). Atlanta, GA: Centers for Disease Control and Prevention.

Fortenberry, J.D., Schick, V., Herbenick, D., Sanders, S., Dodge, B., and Reece, M. (2010). Sexual behaviors and condom use at last vaginal intercourse: a national sample of adolescents ages 14 to 17 years. *Journal of Sexual Medicine*, 7(Suppl.5), 305-314

Goodwin, P.Y., Mosher, W.D. and Chandra, A. (2010). Marriage and cohabitation in the United States: a statistical portrait based on cycle 6 (2002) of the National Survey of Family Growth. National Center for Health Statistics. DHHS Publication No. 2010 – 1980. *Vital Health Statistics*, 23 (28), 1-45.

Halpern-Felsher, B.L., Cornell, J.L., Kropp, R.Y., and Tschann, J.M. (2005). Oral versus vaginal sex among adolescents: perceptions, attitudes, & behaviors. *Pediatrics*, 115 (4), 845-851.

Katz, J., Arias, I., and Beach, S. (Dec. 2000). Psychological abuse, self-esteem and women: dating relationship outcomes. *Psychology of Women Quarterly*, 24 (4), 349-359.

Kaura, S. and Lohman, B. (2007). Dating violence victimization, relationship satisfaction, mental health problems, and acceptability of violence: a comparison of men and women. *Journal of Family Violence*, 22 (6), 367-368.

Kinsey, A., Pomeroy, W., and Martin, C. (1948). *Sexual Behavior in the Human Male.* Philadelphia: Saunders.

Kinsey, A., Pomeroy, W., Martin, C., and Gebhard, P. (1953). *Sexual Behavior in the Human Female.* Philadelphia: Saunders

Lawrence, E. BaYoon, J., MaLanger, A., & MaRo, E. (2009). Is psychological aggression as detrimental as physical aggression? the independent effects of psychological aggression on depression and anxiety symptoms. *Violence & Victims,* 24 (1), 20+.

Mark, K.P., Janssen, E., and Milhausen, R.R. (2011). Infidelity in heterosexual couples: demographic, interpersonal, and personality-related predictors of extradyadic sex. *Archives of Sexual Behavior.* doi: 10.1007/s10508-011-9771-z

Mather, M. and Lauery, D. (2010). *In U.S., proportion married at lowest recorded levels.* Population Reference Bureau. Retrieved January 27, 2011. <http://www.prb.org/articles/2010/usmarriagedecline.aspx.>

Pew Research Center (2010). *The decline of marriage and rise of new families.* Pew Research Center's Social and Demographic Trends Project. Retrieved January 21, 2013. <http://pewsocialtrends.org/files/2010/11/pew-social-trends-2010-families.pdg.>

U.S. Census Bureau (2007, September 19). *Most people make only one trip down the aisle, but first marriages shorter, census bureau reports.* Retrieved January 27, 2013. <http://www.census.gov/PressRelease/www/releases/archives/marital_status_living_ arrangements/010624.html.>

West, A. & Wandrei, M.L. (2002). Intimate partner violence: a model for predicting interventions by informal helpers. *Journal of Interpersonal Violence,* 17, 972-986.

Whisman, M.A. and Snyder, D.K. (2007). Sexual infidelity in a national survey of American women: differences in prevalence and correlation as a function of method of assessment. *Journal of Family Psychology,* 21(2), 147-154.

Zelnick, M., & Kantner, J. (1980). Sexual activity, contraceptive use, and pregnancy among metropolitan-area teenagers: 1971-1979. *Family Planning Perspectives,* 12, 230-237.

PART V

RELATIONSHIPS
AND
COMMUNICATION

WORKSHEET #34

Factors That Influence Communication

The ability of couples to communicate in meaningful ways is essential to the happiness and long-term success of romantic relationships. Good communication skills allow couples to express positive aspects of their relationship to each other, which is likely to strengthen the bond between them. Just as important, if not more so, is the role communication plays in dealing with disagreements and negative feelings when they arise. In fact, the effectiveness of the pattern of communication in a relationship is one of the most accurate predictors of its future success or failure (Clements, Stanley, & Markman, 2004).

Communication Differences between Men and Women

Linguist Deborah Tannen (1990) has done extensive research in the area of communication and gender differences. Her research found that women use less assertiveness than men in their communication. For example, when stating an opinion, women often end their statements with *tag questions* ("That's a good idea, isn't it?"). They also use *disclaimers* ("I may be wrong, but...") and *question statements* ("Don't you think so?"). All of these things tend to decrease the speaker's perceived assertiveness.

Males are less likely than females to discuss their feelings or problems and feel more obligated to offer solutions when someone tells them about a problem – even if the other person is only seeking someone to talk to.

A common topic in communication involves speech quantity. The stereotype is that women talk much more than men. Contrary to popular opinion overall differences in communication are small (Dindia & Canary, 2006). In fact, in public situations, such as meetings or classrooms, men tend to talk more than women. They tend to speak in more lengthy dialogues and interrupt people more than women do. In terms of listening, women tend to more closely listen to the other person, whereas men react only when they agree or disagree (Moore & Davidson, 2000).

Cultural Communication Differences

Some cultures promote individual goals and values whereas others tend to value group needs over that of the individual. The United States and Australia, for example, tend to adopt the most individualistic approach whereas Asian cultures tend to value the group over the individual.

This probably explains why men and women from the United States are more comfortable disclosing personal information to a variety of people whereas people from cultures such as Japan or China, are much less apt to disclose personal information to those outside of their immediate family.

Non Verbal Com is imp

WORKSHEET #34 (CONTINUED)

Nonverbal Communication

Because the majority of our communication is done nonverbally, nonverbal cues are an important part of communication (Knapp & Hall, 2005). Nonverbal communication includes facial expressions, hand gestures, posture, and body positioning. Humans are uniquely designed to read nonverbal cues and respond accordingly.

- *Consider the following words (feelings): scared, worried, bored, sad, angry.*
  How would you demonstrate each of those feelings through body language?

- *"I sure am glad that I'm here today." Say that as though you mean it and then say it as though you do not mean it. How did the two differ?*

WORKSHEET #35

Communication in Romantic Relationships

Eddie and Joanne's Story:

We fight a lot more than the average couple. We yell at each other and then one of us storms out of the house for a few hours. Believe it or not, we love each other and both of us are committed to our relationship.

Michael and Lucy's Story:

Since the day we met our relationship has been easy. We rarely disagree. When a problem does arise, rather than having an argument, Michael goes to the gym and I go to the movies. By the time we each get home, both of us feel better.

Jen and Robert:

We were both children of divorce. We each saw a lot of fighting in our houses growing up and we were determined not to have that kind of relationship. Yes, we have an argument on occasion, but most of the time we address issues before emotions build up. We talk to each other and are usually able to arrive at a compromise.

Research tells us that it is not how much a couple fights, but their *style* of fighting that determines the success of their relationship. By examining a couple's communication and conflict styles, a relationship's outcome can be predicted with near 90% accuracy (Gottman & Levenson, 2002).

It may not seem so on the surface, but all three of the communication patterns described above can be effective in maintaining a healthy, close relationship (Gottman & Silver, 2000).

WORKSHEET #35 (CONTINUED)

Validating Communication (Jen & Robert)

_____

_____

_____

_____

_____

_____

Volatile Communication (Eddie & Joanne)

_____

_____

_____

_____

_____

_____

Conflict-Avoiding Communication (Michael & Lucy)

_____

_____

_____

_____

_____

_____

WORKSHEET #36

Obstacles to Healthy Communication

1. *Criticism* - an attach on your Partners actions

   _____

   _____

   _____

   _____

2. *Contempt* - an attach on your Partners character

   Calling name abuse in many ways.

   _____

   _____

   _____

3. *Overgeneralization*

   "You always" or "You never"

   _____

   _____

   _____

4. *Overkill*

   "If you do that again im leaving"
   Most of the time don't mean it

   _____

   _____

WORKSHEET #36 (CONTINUED)

5. *Defensiveness*

Denying responsibility

6. *Stonewalling*

refusing to engage in Communication
"Silent treatment"

7. *Other?*

8. *Other?*

WORKSHEET #37

Potential Romantic Partners

Whether we realize it or not, each of us has a set of criteria that determines whether or not a person is a potential romantic partner. For example – sex. Some of us would consider only males or only females in our pool of potential romantic partners.

For many of us, the list may change throughout our lives. One might wind up in a relationship with someone who they may have once considered "not their type at all." Conversely, someone's negative experiences with a partner could change their criteria for a future partner.

––––––––––––

You may include or exclude individuals in your field of potential romantic partners not only before you get to know them, but even before you <u>meet</u> them. Rate each item on its importance to you as a criterion in your personal field of potential romantic partners using the following scale:

1. I would absolutely not consider someone who does not meet my requirement on this item.

2. This is very important to me. I'm not sure that I would consider someone who does not meet my requirement.

3. I would definitely consider this, but it would not strongly influence my decision.

4. This is not important to me. It would not factor into my decision when considering someone as a potential romantic partner.

Item	Rating(1-4)
Sex (must be male or female)	
Physical Appearance (must be what I consider to be attractive)	
Age (limit on the number of years older or younger than I am)	
Racial Ethnicity (must have the same racial and/or ethnic background as mine)	

WORKSHEET #37 (CONTINUED)

Item	Rating(1-4)
Personality (must have certain personality characteristics)	
Socioeconomic Background (must come from a family of certain economic and social status)	
Education (must have an educational level at least equal to mine)	
Job or Career (must have a specific type of job or career/or may not have a specific type of job or career)	
Other:	
Other:	
Other:	
Other:	
Other:	

WORKSHEET #38

Building Romantic Relationships

Self-Disclosure

[handwritten: ✷ early disclosures - looked at negativly → ppl who share very personal info too quickly]

What sort of information is safe to disclose when meeting someone?

_____

_____

_____

Similarity

[handwritten: ✷] Which couples are more likely to have a happy relationship? Opposites or those who are similar?

[handwritten: most imp. thing is values] _____

_____

_____

[handwritten: ✷] ***The triangular theory of love*** is researcher Robert Sternberg's theory that three fundamental components of love – intimacy, passion, and commitment – in various combinations, define various types of love relationships (Sternberg, 1986).

The ***intimacy*** component refers to the emotional closeness between two people.

Passion is the sexual and romantic attraction one feels for their partner.

The ***commitment*** component refers to the desire to be loyal and faithful and to commit to maintaining a happy and lasting relationship.

WORKSHEET #38 (CONTINUED)

According to Sternberg, the three components may exist in any combination from none (non-love) to all of them (consummate love).

Consider some of the various combinations that define differing types of love relationships:

Intimacy only

_____

Commitment only

_____

Intimacy and Passion

_____

Passion and Commitment

_____

Commitment and Intimacy

_____

Intimacy, Passion, and Commitment

_____

WORKSHEET #39

Why Relationships End

Romantic relationships are complex and are rarely without periods of distress and dissatisfaction. While some couples work through their difficulties, others are not able to resolve their differences.

Some Reasons Why Relationships Fail
1. *Poor communication*

   _____

   _____

2. *Imbalance of power*

   _____

   _____

3. *Low self-esteem; insecurity*

   _____

   _____

4. *Betrayal of trust*

   _____

   _____

5. *Excessive jealousy*

   _____

   _____

6. *Abuse*

   _____

   _____

WORKSHEET #40

Discussion Questions

1. *What topics should couples address before marriage?*

   Money? i.e. How will finances be handled?

   In-laws? i.e. Where will you spend holidays?

   Careers? i.e. Will both partners work?

   Religion? i.e. How will the children, if any, be raised?

   Other?

2. *What if you learned that your spouse had been unfaithful to you? What factors would influence your desire to maintain or to end the relationship?*

   _____

   _____

   _____

   _____

   _____

   _____

WORKSHEET #41

NAME _____

Read through the following list of statements relating to your ability to initiate and maintain interpersonal relationships. Can you identify any attitudes or behaviors that you would like to change about yourself? Circle the numbers of the items you would most like to change. How might you go about making changes?

Yes   **No**

_____ _____ 1. It's easy for me to compliment others.

_____ _____ 2. I have close friends.

_____ _____ 3. It's easy for me to express affection.

_____ _____ 4. I talk over disagreements with others rather than holding my feelings in or losing my temper.

_____ _____ 5. I can express my feelings to close family or friends.

_____ _____ 6. I can listen to others discussing their feelings without getting uncomfortable.

_____ _____ 7. I can express affection verbally.

_____ _____ 8. I can express thanks or appreciation without feeling uneasy.

_____ _____ 9. I am aware of my feelings.

_____ _____ 10. I enjoy an occasional evening alone.

_____ _____ 11. I can communicate easily with friends.

_____ _____ 12. In general, I love myself.

_____ _____ 13. In general, I am happy with my life.

WORKSHEET #41 (CONTINUED)

Yes   **No**

_____ _____ 14. I can accept the fact that my partner has had other partners before me and I do not worry about how I compare with them.

_____ _____ 15. I try to be open and honest when communicating with others.

_____

_____

_____

_____

_____

_____

PART V: READING

Traditional Marriage Role Reversal

When Paul and Julie Barnes took a family vacation to Washington D.C. with their two children recently, a tour guide asked Paul what he did for a living. Paul answered, "I'm a househusband. I stay at home with the kids." His answer was met with total silence.

According to census and polling data released on May 26, 2013 by the Pew Research Center in their analysis of census and polling data, 4 in 10 American households with children under the age of 18 include a mother who is either the sole or primary earner for her family. This share, which is the highest on record, has quadrupled since 1960. This trend shows no signs of slowing down and is being seen both within and outside of the United States. According to a 2012 article in the Daily Mail newspaper in London, there are 1.4 million men across the United Kingdom whose main role is primary caregiver for their children. In 2008, Fortune Magazine wanted to do a story about househusbands, but they abandoned the project because it was too difficult to find examples of couples for the story. In 2013, of 187 participants at Fortune Magazine's most recent Most Powerful Women in Business Summit, 30% had househusbands.

The recession may have played a role in bringing women into primary earning roles. Many more men than women are employed in industries like construction and manufacturing, both of which take major hits during difficult economic times. Many believe that a major reason behind the trend is society's evolving attitudes regarding gender roles.

The Barnes family had lived in San Francisco for 10 years before moving 5 years ago to Atlanta, where Julie took a job as a vice president of marketing for the Coca-Cola Company. Paul had been a high school math teacher when the family lived in California. While Paul waited for his credentials to be approved so that he could teach in Atlanta, he stayed home with the children. Paul enjoyed it and the couple realized that they could afford to live nicely on one income. Staying at home with their seven-year-old twins, Jake and Emily, seemed to be the best thing for the family.

The implications for the stability of marriages in which the woman is the family breadwinner is not clear. According to the London newspaper article, a third of mothers admit to feeling guilty about going out to work and leaving the children. One in five complain that they are doing two jobs because they have to do housework when they get home from their jobs, and one in ten say that the division of household chores causes marital discord. An ongoing review by economists at the University Of Chicago Booth School of Business, in looking at the distribution of married couples by income of husband versus wife, are finding that couples in which the wife earns more than her husband report less satisfaction and higher rates of divorce. According to the University of Chicago researchers, when the wife brings in more money, couples often revert to more stereotypical sex roles. In such cases, wives typically take on a larger share of household work and childcare. Their arrangement is working very well for Paul and Julie, but even they say that it would not work for every couple.

NAME _____

1. ***What do you see as potential problems in a marital relationship dealing with traditional role reversal?***

2. ***What are the keys to successful role reversal in a marriage?***

_____

_____

_____

_____

_____

_____

_____

_____

_____

_____

_____

_____

_____

_____

_____

_____

_____

_____

_____

_____

_____

_____

_____

,

REFERENCES

Clements, M., Stanley, S., and Markman, H. (2004). Before they said "I do": discriminating among marital outcomes over 13 years. *Journal of Marriage and the Family*, 66, 613-626.

Dindia, K. and Canary, D.J. (2006) (Eds.), *Sex differences and similarities in communication* (2nd ed.). Mahwah, New Jersey: Erlbaum.

Gottman, J. and Silver. N. (2000). *The seven principles for making marriage work*. New York: Crown.

Gottman, J.M. and Levenson, R.W. (2002). A two-factor model for predicting when a couple will divorce: exploratory analysis using 14-year longitudinal data. *Family Process*, 41, 83-95.

Knapp, M.L. and Hall, J.A. (2005). *Nonverbal communication in human interaction* (6th ed.). Belmont, CA: Wadsworth.

Moore, N.B. and Davidson, J.K. (2000). Communicating with new sex partners: college women and questions that make a difference. *Journal of Sex and Marital Therapy*, 26, 215-230.

Sternberg, R.J. (1986). A triangular theory of love. *Psychological Review,* 98, 119-135.

Tannen, D. (1990). *You just don't understand: women and men in conversation*. New York: Ballentine Books.

PART VI

SEXUALLY TRANSMITTED INFECTIONS

WORKSHEET #42 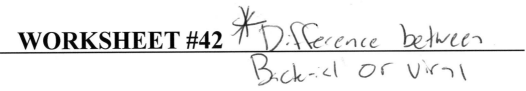 *Difference between Bacterial or viral

Bacterial STIs

Similar to Ghonoriha

Infection: Chlamydia - Bacterial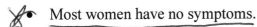

General Facts

- In 2010, 1.3 million cases were reported to the CDC.
- Most women have no symptoms.
- CDC recommends annual screening for sexually active women under the age of 25.
- CDC estimates that women infected with chlamydia are up to five times more likely to become infected with HIV if exposed to it.

Transmission

- Exchange of body fluids through vaginal, anal, or oral sex
- Through childbirth

Symptoms

- Half of all infected men and three quarters of infected women will have no symptoms.
- When symptoms do occur, they usually appear 5 to 21 days after exposure to the bacterium.
- Symptoms include vaginal discharge and bleeding between periods or after intercourse in women; also, pain or burning during urination. In an infected man, the tip of the penis may look red; there may be a discharge from the penis and pain or burning during urination.
- Touching the eyes can result in a bacterial infection that causes inflammation and redness.
- Inflammation of the throat or pain in the anus may occur depending on how the bacterium is contracted.

Treatment or if Left Untreated

- It is treated with antibiotics.
- Untreated infections can result in infections of the urethra in men and pelvic inflammatory disease, infertility, and ectopic pregnancy in women.

fert. egg won't be able to get through   PID Can leave scar tissue

How it is Diagnosed

- Chlamydia testing is not part of a routine annual gynecologic exam.
- It can be detected through a cervical smear in women and by testing the fluid from the penial opening in men.

- Urine test

Infection: Gonorrhea

General Facts

- Most men will show symptoms but most women will not.
- There is evidence that the bacterium that causes gonorrhea is becoming resistant to antibiotic treatment.
- It is very contagious and easily transmitted during sex with an infected partner

Transmission

- Exchange of body fluids through vaginal, anal, or oral sex
- Through childbirth (The use of antibiotic eye drops immediately after birth averts potential complications in the infant of an infected mother.)

Symptoms

- If symptoms appear they usually do so 2 days to 3 to 4 weeks after infection.
- Women experience vaginal discharge, pain or burning during urination, and abdominal or lower back pain; men experience a discharge from the penis, more frequent urination, and burning during urination.

Treatment <u>or</u> if Left Untreated

- It is treated with <u>antibiotics</u>.
- Untreated infections can lead to infertility in women and men and increased susceptibility to HIV.

How it is Diagnosed

- Gonorrhea testing is not part of a routine annual gynecologic exam.
- It can be detected through a cervical smear in women and by testing the fluid from the penial opening in men.

Infection: Syphilis— Bacterial antibiotics

General Facts

- The prevalence of syphilis peaked in the late 1940s, but began to decline with the discovery of penicillin.
- The overall syphilis rate in the U.S. reached an all-time low in 2000, but has since begun to rise again.

Syphilis (Cont'd)

- CDC data shows a dramatic increase in syphilis especially in young black men.

Transmission

- The bacterium that causes syphilis (treponema pallidum commonly called a spirochete) is transmitted almost exclusively from direct contact with the syphilis sore, usually by oral, anal, or vaginal intercourse, or by touching the infected area.

 Syphilis is most contagious during its early stages.

- An infected pregnant woman can transmit the bacterium during pregnancy or childbirth.

- The syphilis rate among infants in 2000 declined by 51 percent since 1997, the year before the Centers for Disease Control and Prevention (CDC) launched a national campaign to eliminate the disease in the United States. In 2000, only 529 cases of congenital syphilis (CS) (13.4 cases per 100,000 live births) were reported in the United States, compared to 1,077 cases, (27.8 cases per hundred thousand live births) in 1997.

- This decline in congenital syphilis has significantly improved infant health in the United States.

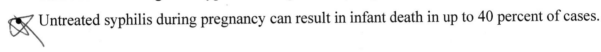 Untreated syphilis during pregnancy can result in infant death in up to 40 percent of cases.

Symptoms

- When a person comes into contact with the syphilis infection, the spirochetes enter into the body and incubate for 2 to 3 weeks, after which a painless sore (a chancre) appears at the point of infection.

- In this **primary phase,** the sore most commonly appears on the inner vaginal walls or cervix in women. It may also appear on the external genitals, particularly the labia. In men, the chancre most often appears on the glans of the penis, but it may also show up on the penile shaft or on the scrotum.

- The sores can also appear on the lips, tongue, anus, breasts, or fingers.

- The chancre usually lasts for 2 to 6 weeks and heals without leaving a scar.

- In the **secondary phase**, which usually occurs 2 to 8 weeks after exposure, a copper colored skin rash appears on the body, often on the palms of the hands and soles of the feet. The person may also experience flu-like symptoms, including fever, joint inflammation, and headache. As the lesions of the rash burst, they release a discharge that is very contagious. This phase can last from a few weeks to more than a year – and the symptoms may disappear and reappear throughout that time.

WORKSHEET #42 (CONTINUED)

Syphilis – *Symptoms* (Cont'd)

Don't have symptoms

- When the symptoms of secondary syphilis disappear, the person goes into the ***latent stage*** that can last for years. During this time there may be no symptoms, but the spirochetes are still in the body multiplying and invading organs. After a year in the latent stage, the infected individual is no longer contagious to others. The exception is a pregnant woman with syphilis who can pass the infection to her fetus in any stage.

- The syphilis bacteria can lie dormant for many years. Many people will have no further symptoms. Approximately 15% of individuals who are not treated during the first three stages of syphilis eventually develop ***tertiary syphilis***. In this final stage of syphilis, which can occur 10 to 20 years after initial infection, the infected individual can develop heart failure, blindness, paralysis, and severe mental disturbance, finally resulting in death.

Treatment or if Left Untreated

- Syphilis is treated with antibiotics (usually penicillin).
- Untreated syphilis can lead to the development of tertiary syphilis and death.

How it is Diagnosed

- Syphilis is diagnosed with a blood test.

WORKSHEET #43

Viral Infections – Herpes — Virus

General Facts

- Herpes is caused by the herpes simplex virus (HSV). Eight different herpes viruses infect humans, causing diseases such as chickenpox, shingles, and mononucleosis.
- Herpes simplex virus type 1 (HSV-1) *Oral* and herpes simplex virus type 2 (HSV-2) *genital* are the two herpes viruses that are widely transmitted through sexual contact.
- HSV-1 usually affects the mouth or lips – called cold sores or fever blisters; HSV-2 usually affects the genitals.
- Herpes may be spread from one part of the body to another.
- Most people get oral herpes through nonsexual contact. Children, for example, might get it by sharing a cup with an infected individual.
- Genital herpes, which is more likely to be spread through sexual contact, affects the genitals or the anal area.
- According to the CDC, more than 100 million people in the U.S. have oral herpes and at least 45 million have genital herpes.
- HSV-2 is twice as common in women as in men, suggesting that male to female transmission is more likely than female to male transmission.
- Once you are infected, you have the virus for life.

Transmission

- Herpes is spread through skin to skin contact with an infected person.
- Genital herpes (HSV-2) is transmitted primarily through penile-vaginal, oral-genital, genital-anal, or anal-anal contact.
- The mucous membranes of the genitals, mouth, rectum, and the eyes are most prone to infection.
- Although genital and oral herpes are usually associated with different herpes viruses, HSV-1 can affect the genital area, and HSV-2 can produce a lesion in the mouth.
- An uninfected woman has a significantly higher risk of getting herpes from an infected man than an uninfected man has of getting herpes from an infected woman. This may be because women have more mucosal surface area in their genitals than men.
- Having the HSV-2 virus affords the person almost complete protection from getting
- HSV-1; having the HSV-1 virus offers limited protection against infection with HSV-2.

WORKSHEET #43 (CONTINUED)

- Herpes does not survive for a long period of time outside of the body. However, it is possible for the virus to survive for several hours if it is residing in a warm, moist environment (a towel for example). The risk of transmission by this route is very low.

- When any herpes sores are present, the person is highly contagious.

- It was once believed that it could be transmitted only when lesions were present. It is now known that HSV can be transmitted even when there are no lesions.

- The virus may also be transmitted during childbirth.

Symptoms

- The symptoms associated with HSV-1 and HSV-2 are very similar.

- The herpes virus enters the body through nerve endings that supply the skin. It then travels to nerves near the spinal cord.

- Though the virus is in the body, many people have few, or even no symptoms.

- If symptoms do occur, they usually appear one to three weeks after the virus enters the body.

- In addition to flu-like symptoms during the first outbreak, symptoms consist of one or more red, itchy, painful bumps, called papules, around the genitals, anus, lips, mouth, tongue, or throat.

- Soon after they appear, the papules turn into small fluid filled blisters filled with active virus.

- The wet, painful open sores are surrounded by a red ring. The person is highly contagious at this time.

- The sores last for one to four weeks. They then form scabs, drop-off and heal.

- Although the sores heal, the virus remains in the body.

- The virus lies inactive in spinal nerves near the infected site.

- Periodically the virus may travel back to the surface of the skin, causing a recurrence (often called an outbreak).

- Some people never experience a recurrence of herpes following their initial episode.

- Most people, however, will experience at least one recurrence; some will experience occasional outbreaks; others may do so frequently.

- During a recurrence, sores can appear in any part of the body supplied by the infected nerve.

- A number of factors can trigger the reactivation of the herpes virus, including emotional stress, fatigue, fever, menstruation, and exposure to sunlight.

WORKSHEET #43 (CONTINUED)

Treatment or if Left Untreated

- There is no cure for herpes.

- Those who have frequent occurrences (more than six per year) may elect to take the antiviral medication, acyclovir, which interferes with the ability of the virus to replicate. Medications used to treat herpes function to decrease the number, severity, and duration of outbreaks and lessen the shedding of the virus.

How it is Diagnosed

- A health professional can swab the herpes sore so that the contents can be analyzed.

- A blood test can show if antibodies to HSV exist.

- A visual test can be used if symptoms exist.

WORKSHEET #44

Viral Infections – Viral Hepatitis — *infection of liver*

(handwritten annotations: ① infection of liver; ② Vacine)

General Facts

- Hepatitis is an infection of the liver.

- There are several types of viral hepatitis. The type which is most likely to be transmitted sexually is hepatitis B.

- In the U.S. more than 40,000 adults and children become infected with hepatitis B virus (HBV) each year.

Transmission

- Hepatitis B can be transmitted through blood or blood products, semen, vaginal secretions, and saliva.

- An infected mother can transmit a hepatitis B infection to her baby at birth.

- HBV is not transmitted through casual contact.

Symptoms

- Up to 50% of those with HBV have no symptoms.

- When symptoms do occur, they generally occur one to four months after infection.

- Early symptoms include mild flu-like symptoms such as fever, fatigue, poor appetite, achiness, and diarrhea.

- Later symptoms include a yellowing of the skin and the whites of the eyes (jaundice), abdominal pain, dark urine, and pale colored feces.

- The vast majority of individuals (90 to 95%) with HBV clear the infection on their own (acute hepatitis).

- Full recovery is usually complete within six months after infection.

- Once the infection is cleared, the individual cannot be reinfected and the infection cannot be transmitted to others.

- Five to ten percent of individuals with HBV are not able to clear the infection from their body.

- These individuals are capable of infecting others throughout their lives.

- About one third of those with chronic hepatitis B are at risk of developing serious complications including cirrhosis of the liver (destruction of healthy liver cells and development of nonfunctional scar tissue) and liver cancer.

WORKSHEET #44 (CONTINUED

Treatment or if Left Untreated

- No effective treatment is known to treat hepatitis B.

- It is recommended that infected individuals get plenty of rest, eat a healthy diet, and avoid drugs and alcohol.

- Some individuals with chronic hepatitis B are given medication to improve their liver function and reduce the severity of symptoms.

- Pregnant women who are infected with HBV are likely to pass the infection to the fetus.

- The overwhelming majority of infants born to women infected with HBV will become infected with chronic hepatitis – unless treated very soon after birth.

- A vaccine to prevent hepatitis B infection has been available since 1982.

How it is Diagnosed

- Hepatitis B is diagnosed with a blood test which will show the presence of antibodies formed in response to the infection.

WORKSHEET #45

STI FACT SHEET

NAME _____

In each block, cross out any statement which is incorrect. (In any box both statements may be correct; one may be correct and one incorrect; or both may be incorrect.)

	General Facts	**Symptoms & Complications**	**Diagnosis & Treatment**
Chlamydia	• most women show no symptoms • it is a ~~viral~~ infection *Baterial*	• inflammation of the eyes • inflammation of the throat	• ~~no effective treatment is available~~ *antibiotics* • ~~testing is part of a routine exam~~
Gonorrhea	• most ~~men~~ show *Women* no symptoms • it can be transmitted through childbirth	• women – burning during urination • men – burning during urination	• it is treated with antibiotics • the bacterium is becoming resistant to treatment
Syphilis	• ~~new cases are at an all time low~~ *Beginning to rise* • it can be transmitted to the fetus during pregnancy	• a very painful sore appears at the point infection • ~~latent stage lasts for six months at most~~	*treated w/ antibiotic* *Blood test*
Herpes	• ~~most people get oral herpes through sexual contact, i.e. oral sex~~ *non Sexual contact* • about 45 million people in the U.S. have genital herpes	• ~~when sores appear, person is no longer contagious~~ *Highly contagious* • after sores heal, virus still remains in the body	• ~~antiviral meds can cure herpes in uncomplicated cases~~ *NO cure* • ~~oral herpes cannot cannot be transmitted to the genitals~~ *it Can*
Hepatitis B	• it is an infection of of the liver • adults and children can become infected with hepatitis B	• 90-95% of those infected clear the infection on their own • ~~those who do not are capable of infecting others throughout their lives~~	• it can be diagnosed with a blood test • ~~a vaccine to prevent hepatitis B is not yet available~~ *there is a Vaccine*

WORKSHEET #46

Viral Infections – Human Papilloma Virus

General Facts

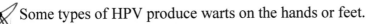

- Human papilloma virus (HPV) is the world's most common sexually transmitted virus.
- There are more than 100 strains of HPV, most of which are harmless and produce no symptoms.
- Some types of HPV produce warts on the hands or feet.
- The various strains remain at the site in which they cause infection, so warts on the hands cannot be transmitted to the genitals or anywhere else on the body.
- More than 30 strains of the virus are sexually transmitted.
- Up to 20 million people in the U.S. are currently infected with sexually transmitted HPV, and more than 6 million Americans become newly infected each year.
- Low-risk strains of the virus cause genital warts.
- High-risk strains of the virus do not produce genital warts, but can place one at increased risk to develop cancer of the cervix, vagina, penis, anus, mouth, or throat.
- While there is no cure for HPV, the vast majority of people (90%) will clear the infection on their own. As many as 80% of sexually active Americans will have had an HPV infection at some point in their lives.
- The HPV virus can lie dormant for years with no symptoms. The appearance of an HPV infection just means that the person contracted HPV at some time in their life.

Transmission

- HPV can be transmitted by oral, anal, and vaginal sex, and by skin-to-skin contact (HPV likes to live in the part of the skin which is very close to the surface).
- It is possible though not common to transmit HPV from mother to baby during childbirth.
- HPV is most commonly transmitted by individuals who are without symptoms and do not realize they are infected.

Symptoms

- Genital warts are the most common visible signs of HPV infection.
- Genital warts can be caused by several of the low-risk strains of HPV.
- They're very contagious and are spread by skin-to-skin contact during sexual activity.
- People infected with a type of HPV that causes genital warts will usually show no outward symptoms.

WORKSHEET #46 (CONTINUED)

- Those who do show symptoms will develop painless, flesh-colored bumps which vary in size, shape, and number.

- They will usually appear anywhere from several weeks to six months after infection.

- While they appear most often on the cervix in women or in the urethra in men, they may show up anywhere on the genitals, or in the anal region, or even on the upper thighs.

- Warts often disappear on their own though the virus still remains in the body and may cause recurrences at some point in the future.

Treatment or if Left Untreated

- Genital warts may be removed if so desired.

- The decision to have the warts removed is typically made either because they produce discomfort or the appearance is unsettling to the individual.

- Removing the warts does not mean that they may not return nor does it necessarily lower the chance of passing the virus onto a sexual partner.

- Treatments for removing the warts include cryotherapy (freezing) with liquid nitrogen; topical application of medicated cream; and laser surgery.

- Genital warts may disappear without any treatment.

- Gardasil is a vaccine that protects against the particular types of human papilloma virus that cause 70% of cervical cancers.

- The vaccine is approved for males and females between the ages of 9 and 26. It consists of three injections given over a period of six months.

- Gardasil does not protect against all strains of HPV that cause cancer, but it does provide protection against the two strains that cause 70% of cervical cancers (HPV 16 and 18).

- At this time it appears that the vaccine provides 10 to 15 years of protection in women.

- In males, the vaccine has only been tested for a short time so it isn't clear how long protection will last but the level of protection against the cancers seems to significantly drop after two years.

- There have been a very small number of cases of Guillain-Barre syndrome associated with the administration of Gardasil.

- Guillain-Barre syndrome is a disorder of the body's immune system which can affect the neuromuscular system, producing muscle weakness and even temporary paralysis. Guillain-Barre is a rare disorder which can be triggered by any vaccine.

- Researchers at the CDC as well as the FDA consider Gardasil to be safe and effective.

WORKSHEET #46 (CONTINUED)

How it is Diagnosed

- Infection with HPV is usually diagnosed by the appearance of genital warts or by an abnormal Pap test in women.

- However, some Pap tests do not detect cancer of the cervix. A more sensitive test is the COBAS test.

- The COBAS test consists of a Pap test and an HPV (DNA) test that determines if a woman has the high risk strains (HPV 16/18) that can lead to cervical cancer with one specimen.

- An accurate test for males is not yet available.

- HPV is often present with no visible symptoms.

- A blood test can detect the presence of the human papilloma virus in women; no tests are available for men.

- HPV tests are not given routinely because the virus is so prevalent and most people clear the infection on their own.

HPV Linked to Cancer

- Over a dozen types of human papilloma virus are classified as high risk viruses.

- These high risk viruses place individuals at increased risk of developing cancer of the cervix, vagina, penis, anus, mouth, and throat.

- Human papilloma virus is present in an overwhelming percentage of cervical cancer tumors.

 Still, most high-risk HPV infections do not progress to cancer.

- Most women will clear the virus from their bodies. Some, however, will maintain a persistent infection with a high risk strain of HPV.

- A Pap test, performed during a gynecologic exam, will detect precancerous changes to the cervix; fortunately, cervical cancer is typically a slow-growing cancer.

- The American College of Obstetricians and Gynecologists recommends that women get tested every two years until the age of 30. After reaching the age of 30, it is recommended that women get tested every three years.

- Regular gynecologic screening which includes a Pap test is responsible for a steady and significant reduction in deaths from cervical cancer.

- Penile cancer is rare, but men infected with HPV are at increased risk for its development.

- Individuals infected with HPV are much more likely to develop cancers of the mouth and throat than those without the virus; having oral sex with someone infected with a high risk strain of HPV increases one's risk of these cancers.

WORKSHEET #47

HPV Vaccine: Differing Viewpoints

The HPV vaccine, known as Gardasil, protects against four HPV types, two of which are responsible for causing cervical cancer. When approved by the Food and Drug Administration (FDA), vaccination was recommended for girls between the ages of nine and twelve. Some feel that vaccination at an early age is important to insure that girls may be immunized before they contract HPV. However, some feel that it is inappropriate to vaccinate youngsters against a sexually transmitted infection.

Points in Favor of Recommended Vaccination	**Points Against Recommended Vaccination**

Suppose that you are faced with the decision of whether or not to allow your child to receive the HPV vaccine, Gardasil. Would you want your child to be immunized? If yes, at what age?

_____

_____

_____

_____

WORKSHEET #48

Viral Infections – HIV / AIDS

General Facts

- HIV is the human immunodeficiency virus. It is the virus that can lead to Acquired Immune Deficiency Syndrome, or AIDS.

- There are two types of HIV: HIV-1 and HIV-2. In the United States, the term HIV primarily refers to HIV-1.

- There are more than 34 million people worldwide who are living with HIV/AIDS (Amfar, 2012).

- HIV attacks and destroys cells of the immune system known as CD_4 or helper T-cells. CD_4 cells play a central role in helping the body fight disease.

- CD_4 cells coordinate the immune system's response to invaders such as bacteria, viruses, or cancer cells.

- As the immune system becomes weaker the body succumbs to infections and diseases that it would normally be able to fight.

- There were 2.7 million new HIV infections worldwide in 2010, including an estimated 390,000 among children (UNAIDS, 2011).

- More than 2/3 (69%) of all people living with HIV live in sub-Saharan Africa.

- The Centers for Disease Control (CDC) estimates 1.1 million people in the U.S. are living with HIV infection and one in five of them are unaware of their infection (CDC, 2012).

- Since the epidemic began, an estimated 1,129,127 people in the U.S. have been diagnosed with AIDS.

- The incidence of HIV/AIDS is increasing most rapidly in women, minorities, and men who have sex with men (MSM).

- Blacks represented approximately 14% of the US population, but accounted for an estimated 44% of new HIV infections in 2009.

- Hispanics represented 16% of the population but accounted for 20% of the new HIV infections in 2009.

- The numbers for minority women are particularly disturbing. While black and Hispanic women together represent less than a quarter of all women in the United States, they account for 75% of reported cases of AIDS in women.

WORKSHEET #48 (CONTINUED)

Transmission

- HIV is transmitted through direct contact of a mucous membrane with the following fluids or exchange of the following fluids: blood, semen, vaginal fluid, and cerebrospinal fluid. HIV is also present in breast milk.

- There is absolutely no evidence that HIV is spread through sweat, tears, urine, feces, or mosquito bites.

- The virus is present in saliva, but in very low amounts. It is said that it would take an exchange of more than a gallon of infected saliva with blood, semen, or vaginal fluid to effectively transmit HIV.

- Sexual contact is the most common behavior by which HIV is transmitted.

- HIV may be transmitted through oral, anal, or vaginal sex.

- Unprotected anal sex is a particularly high risk behavior because of the likelihood of tearing of rectal tissue.

- While unprotected male-to-male sexual contact is the most common cause of new infection in the U.S., worldwide most HIV infections are acquired through unprotected heterosexual sex with an infected partner.

- Unprotected heterosexual intercourse is the primary means by which women are infected, both in the United States and worldwide.

- A female is twice as likely to contract HIV from an infected male partner than a male is to contract HIV from an infected female partner during unprotected vaginal intercourse.

- Women have more mucosal surface area in their genital area than men.

- The virus is more heavily concentrated in semen compared to vaginal fluid.

- Unprotected receptive sexual acts are more susceptible to transmission than unprotected insertive sexual acts.

- HIV may be transmitted through contact with contaminated needles.

- The testing of pregnant women and treatment for those who are infected have resulted in a dramatic decline in the number of children infected with HIV during pregnancy, labor and delivery, or breast-feeding (perinatal transmission).

- Perinatal transmission is the source of almost all AIDS cases in children in the U.S.

- Most of the children with AIDS in the United States are black or Hispanic.

- HIV does not survive well outside of the body and is not spread by casual contact.

WORKSHEET #48 (CONTINUED)

Symptoms

- Two to four weeks after an individual is exposed to human immunodeficiency virus, he or she may experience flu-like symptoms, such as fever, headache, nausea, and diarrhea.

- During this ***acute infection phase*** the virus replicates very rapidly. The viral load (the amount of HIV in the blood) rises rapidly.

- Though very infectious at this stage, an individual may not test as HIV- positive since it usually takes about three months for the body to produce enough antibodies to the virus to be detected with a blood test.

- Following the acute infection stage, the person infected with HIV may have no symptoms. This is called the ***asymptomatic*** or ***latency stage.*** During this time, though the individual has no obvious symptoms, the virus continues to multiply and to destroy cells in the immune system. Because the immune system is making an effort to subdue the virus, the viral load is not as high as it is in the acute infection stage. Even so, the HIV-positive individual can still transmit the virus to others. This asymptomatic stage lasts an average of 10 years, but it can be as brief as a few months and as long as 20+ years.

- In a healthy individual, the CD_4 cell count is 800 or greater.

- As time passes, the infected persons CD_4 cell count continues to drop, resulting in a progressively weaker immune system.

- As the immune system continues to become less functional, symptoms begin to appear. Early symptoms associated with HIV infection include fatigue, weight loss, a characteristic infection in the mouth, and skin rash.

- If the HIV infected individual has not already begun to be treated with antiretroviral medication, symptoms often begin when the CD_4 cell count drops below 500 and the viral load rises.

- As the disease progresses, more severe symptoms such as night sweats, recurrent diarrhea, cough, and fever begin to appear. There may be rapid weight loss. The individual may experience a thick, whitish coating in the mouth, called thrush, which is indicative of an oral yeast infection.

- Without treatment with medication, it takes an average of 10 years after infection for a person to develop AIDS. However, this number is greatly variable.

- The progression depends on many factors, including an individual's viral load, their overall immune system function, and their access to high-quality health care.

WORKSHEET #48 (CONTINUED)

How it is Diagnosed

- In the U.S. the diagnosis of AIDS is made if the HIV-positive individual develops a CD_4 cell count of less than 200 cells per microliter of blood or history of AIDS defining illnesses, which include nearly 30 opportunistic infections that do not normally sicken healthy people.

- Because of their impaired immune systems, AIDS patients are more likely to develop cancer than someone who does not have AIDS. Everyone has cells that mutate and may become cancerous, but a healthy immune system will recognize the changes and attack the cells. AIDS patients are particularly prone to lymphomas, cervical cancer, cancer of the digestive system, and the type of skin cancer known as Karposi's sarcoma.

- Once infected with HIV, one's immune system will begin to produce antibodies to fight the virus.

- This process is known as seroconversion.

- The time it takes for a person to produce enough antibodies to be detected varies.

- Antibodies typically will be detectable within 6 to 12 weeks, but it may take as long as six months.

- Antibodies to the HIV virus may be detected in blood, saliva, or urine.

- The most common HIV tests use blood, oral fluid, or urine to detect HIV antibodies in the body. Results from enzyme immunoassay (EIA) tests can take up to two weeks. Rapid HIV antibody test results can take 10 to 20 minutes.

- If an individual gets a positive result from either of these tests, another test called the Western blot test is given to confirm the result.

Antigen Tests

These tests are not as common as and more costly than antibody tests, but they can be used to diagnose HIV infection earlier – from one to three weeks after one is first infected with HIV. Antigen tests require a blood sample.

Babies born to HIV-positive mothers are tested with a special PCR test, because their blood contains their mother's HIV antibodies for several months. This means they would test HIV-positive on a standard antibody test – but a PCR test can determine whether the babies have the virus itself.

Blood supplies in most developed countries are screened for HIV using PCR tests. PCR tests are also used to measure *viral loads* for people who are HIV-positive.

WORKSHEET #48 (CONTINUED)

Anonymous vs. Confidential Testing

- HIV testing can be anonymous or confidential.

   1. In an anonymous test no personal identifying information is given and there is no official record of the result. The tester is the only one who will know the result. The person being tested is given a code that is impossible to trace.

   2. In a confidential test, the tester, certain clinical staff members, and at times, public health officials, will be aware of the test results.

   3. Home kits are available in which a person pricks his or her own finger and dabs blood on a treated card which is mailed to a laboratory. Testers are given an ID number and may call to receive their anonymous result.

Treatment or if Left Untreated

- There is no cure for HIV/AIDS nor is there a vaccine against the virus, however, a number of antiretroviral drugs have greatly increased the life expectancy of an individual with HIV/AIDS.

Treatment or if Left Untreated

- Drugs known as nucleoside reverse transcriptase inhibitors, such as AZT, interrupt viral replication at an early stage. This results in slowing the spread of HIV in the body, increasing the CD_4 cell count, delaying the occurrence of opportunistic infections, and decreasing the rate of transmission from mother to fetus.

- Another class of drugs, known as protease inhibitors, interrupts the virus from copying itself at a later stage in its life cycle.

- Other drugs interfere with HIV's ability to enter cells.

- A medical treatment called highly active antiretroviral therapy (HAART) was introduced in 1996. HAART consists of three or more antiretroviral drugs. It has significantly increased the lifespan of individuals with HIV/AIDS. This type of combination therapy has proven effective at reducing the development of drug-resistant strains of HIV.

- As beneficial as these drugs are, patients on this type of therapy suffer from many side effects, including nausea and vomiting, cardiovascular problems, and nerve damage.

- Additionally, combination drug therapy can be very expensive. It is estimated that medication, alone, can cause some patients $25,000 per year.

WORKSHEET #49

AIDS Orphans in Sub-Saharan Africa

In 2009, 16.6 million children worldwide had lost one or both parents to AIDS (AIDS orphans). Ninety percent of them were from sub-Saharan Africa even though only 10% of the world's population lives there (UNAIDS, 2010). AIDS orphans are often very young – 15% are newborns to 4 years old; 35% are 5 to 9 years old; and 50% are 10 to 14 years old..

Given the high rate of HIV/AIDS in sub-Saharan Africa, it is very important to find ways to reduce HIV/AIDS infections, to increase access to treatment, and to provide assistance for AIDS orphans.

What is the primary mode of HIV transmission in sub-Saharan Africa?

_____

_____

_____

_____

1. What can be done to decrease infection in that part of the world?

   _____

   _____

   _____

2. Should the United States provide assistance to those affected by HIV/AIDS in sub-Saharan Africa? Why or why not?

   _____

   _____

   _____

PART VI: READING

A Baby with HIV Is "Functionally Cured"

At the 2013 Conference on Retroviral and Opportunistic Infections in Atlanta, doctors announced that a baby had been "functionally cured" of HIV infection for the first time.

A "functional cure" is when the presence of the virus is so small treatment is not necessary and standard clinical tests cannot detect the virus in the blood.

All HIV-positive mothers will pass antibodies to the virus to their babies. Without treatment, about 30% of mothers will transmit the actual virus. HIV-positive mothers given appropriate treatment pass the virus on in less than 2% of cases. If the mother's HIV infection is not under control, the infant would be given anti-retroviral drugs at preventive doses for six weeks to prevent infection and then therapy would begin if HIV is diagnosed.

When the Mississippi baby was about a day old, doctors tested for the presence of the virus. Early positive tests suggested not only the presence of HIV infection, but that it occurred during the pregnancy. Doctors decided to immediately use an aggressive three day regimen within 70 hours of her birth.

The baby's mother had received no prenatal care and was not diagnosed as HIV-positive until just before delivery. Doctors administered the drugs as they did in hopes of controlling the virus.

Viral levels dropped rapidly with treatment and, in fact, were undetectable by the time the baby was a month old. This remained the case for about a year and a half, after which time the mother, inexplicably, stopped giving her baby the drugs. When the mother returned to the hospital with her baby five months later, doctors expected to see high levels of virus. Instead, the tests were negative.

This is the first documented case in which the baby was infected and then after a period of treatment has been able to go off treatment without a rise in her viral level. Now 2 ½, the child has been off medications for a year with no sign of HIV.

If further study shows that this works for other babies, it can have worldwide implications. The World Health Organization estimates that 430,000 children were newly infected with HIV in 2007 and 90% of them were infected through mother to child transmission.

NAME _____

Mother-to-child transmission is rare in the US. When HIV/AIDS was first identified and for many years after, HIV/AIDS was called a problem for the "4H club" (hemophiliacs*, heroin users, homosexual men and Haitians*).

*Hemophilia is a rare bleeding disorder in which the blood doesn't clot normally. People with hemophilia are more likely to require blood transfusions than people in the general population.

Why were these particular groups classified as high risk?

Do you see any problems identifying certain groups of people as "high risk groups"?

_____

_____

_____

_____

_____

_____

_____

_____

_____

_____

_____

_____

_____

_____

_____

_____

REFERENCES

AIDS.gov. *HIV Test Types.* Last updated Feb. 9, 2012. Web. 13 Dec. 2012.
  <http://aids.gov/hiv-aids-basics/prevention/hiv-testing/hiv-test-types/>

American Foundation for AIDS Research. *Statistics: Worldwide.* Last updated Nov. 2012.
  AMFAR. Web. 13 Dec. 2012.
  <http://www.amfar.org/about_hiv_and_aids/facts_and_stats/statistics_worldwide/

Centers for Disease Control and Prevention. *Basic Information about HIV and AIDS.* Last
  reviewed April 11, 2012. *CDC.* Web. 13 Dec. 2012.
  <http://www.cdc.gov/hiv/topics/basic/print/index.htm>

Centers for Disease Control and Prevention. *HIV in the United States: An Overview- Centers for
  Disease Control.* August 2011. *CDC.* Web. 13 Dec. 2012.
  <http://www.cdc.gov/hiv/topics/surveillance/resources/factsheets/pdf/HIV-US-overview>

Centers for Disease Control and Prevention. *HIV in the United States: At a Glance.* July 2012.
  CDC. Web. 30 Dec. 2012.
  <www.cdc.gov/hiv/resources/factsheets/PDF/HIV_at_a_glance.pdf>

Centers for Disease Control and Prevention. *STD Trends in the United States: 2010 National Data
  for Gonorrhea, Chlamydia, and Syphilis.* Last updated: Nov. 17, 2011. *CDC.* Web. 13 Dec. 2012.
  <http://www.cdc.gov/std/stats10/trends.htm>

Centers for Disease Control and Prevention. *Syphilis Among Infants Down More Than Half in
  Three Years.* July 2001. *CDC.* Web. 20 March 2013.
  <http://www.cdc.gov/std/press/presscsyph7-2001.htm>

Giuliano, A.R., Palefsky, J.M., Goldstone, S., Moreira, E.D., Penny, M.E., Aranda, C., and Guris, D.
  (2011). The efficacy of quadrivalent HPV vaccine against HPV infection and disease in males.
  New England Journal of Medicine, 354, 401-411.

UNAIDS. *UNAIDS Report on the global AIDS epidemic 2010.* Web. 12 Oct. 2013.
  <www.unaids.org/globalreport/global_report.htm>

UNAIDS. *2011 UNAIDS World AIDS Day Report: Intensifying Our Efforts to Eliminate
  HIV/AIDS.* Web. 12 Oct. 2013.
  <www.unaids.org/en/media/unaids/contentassests/documents/unaidspublication/2011/
  jc2216 _worldaidsday_re...>

PART VII

CONTRACEPTION

WORKSHEET #50

Hormonal Methods of Contraception

Oral Contraceptives ("birth control pills")

Oral contraceptives, often referred to as birth control pills, are among the most popular reversible birth control methods used by women in the United States (Hatcher et al., 2008). Oral contraceptives fall into two major categories: combination pills and mini-pills.

How They Work

Combination oral contraceptives contain both estrogen and progestin. The progestin-only "mini-pills" have slightly different mechanisms of action and side effects than combination oral contraceptives. The contraceptive mechanism of action in oral contraceptives is the prevention of ovulation. The daily dose of estrogen and progestin in the combination pills alter the body's normal hormonal cycle which typically prevents the release of an egg (ovulation). The pills also increase the acidity and thickness of the cervical mucus. The thickened mucus makes it more difficult for sperm to penetrate into the uterus. Even if an egg were somehow to mature, sperm would be unlikely to survive the passage through the cervix. Finally, the combination oral contraceptives inhibit the development of the inner lining of the uterus (the endometrium), making the implantation of a fertilized egg unlikely.

How They Are Taken

A woman takes one combination oral contraceptive pill each day for 21 days, and then either no pill or a placebo for the remaining seven days of the typical 28 day cycle. It is important to take a pill every day, preferably at the same time. If a woman forgets to take a pill, she should take it as soon as she remembers. If she forgets to take her pill for more than a day, she should continue taking the rest of her packet of pills, but a back-up method of birth control should be used during that cycle.

Instead of the traditional 21 day hormone cycle, there are birth control pills specifically designed to be taken continuously which eliminates the menstrual period for months at a time. The pill marketed under the brand name Seasonale is taken once a day for three months followed by seven placebo pills, during which time bleeding occurs. Another pill, Seasonique, includes a low dose of estrogen during the seven "off" days to lessen the occurrence of bleeding (Sulak, 2007). Still another brand, Lybrel, may be taken continuously for a year (McCarthy & Brar, 2008).

WORKSHEET #50 (CONTINUED)

These products may be beneficial to women who experience painful periods, heavy bleeding, cycle-related migraine headaches, or other debilitating menstruation-related conditions. There is no medical evidence that a woman needs to bleed monthly. While there are no known health risks associated with extended cycles, their long-term effects are not known.

Effectiveness of Oral Contraceptives

Birth control pills provide one of the most effective methods of preventing pregnancy. With perfect use, only one woman in a thousand (0.1%) will become pregnant while using combination oral contraceptives. For the progestin-only "mini-pill," only five women in a thousand should expect an accidental pregnancy.

However, many women forget to take a pill from time to time or may take drugs that interfere with the pill's effectiveness. Even with less than perfect use, such as an occasional missed pill, only approximately three percent of women may become pregnant each year when using combination oral contraceptives.

Advantages

1. When used properly, they are nearly 100 percent effective.

2. They help to regulate the menstrual cycle and reduce menstrual cramping.

3. The combination pill reduces the risks of endometrial and ovarian cancers.

_____

_____

_____

_____

_____

_____

WORKSHEET #50 (CONTINUED)

Disadvantages

1. The birth control pill provides no protection against STIs.

2. Some women experience side effects such as nausea and vomiting, fluid retention, tenderness in the breasts and weight gain.

3. Those with a history of circulatory problems or stroke are typically advised not to use the pill since it may increase blood pressure and the risk of blood clots in some women.

_____

_____

_____

_____

Commonly Asked Questions

1. Are birth control pills a popular form of contraception?

   Answer: _____

   _____

   _____

   _____

2. Does the use of birth-control pills place a woman at increased risk of breast cancer?

   Answer: _____

   _____

   _____

   _____

WORKSHEET #50 (CONTINUED)

3. Are there any psychological side effects associated with birth control pill use?

    Answer: _____

    _____

    _____

    _____

4. Are there any situations in which a woman should not be on the pill at all?

    Answer: _____

    _____

    _____

    _____

    _____

    _____

    _____

    _____

5. Are there any medications that interfere with the effectiveness of the birth control pill?

    Answer: _____

    _____

    _____

    _____

6. Can the birth control pill be prescribed to anyone or are there restrictions having to do with age and/or parental consent?

    Answer: _____

    _____

    _____

    _____

7. How much time will it take for a woman to be able to get pregnant once she stops using birth control pills?

    Answer: _____

    _____

    _____

    _____

Other Forms of Hormonal Contraception

Ortho Evra is a thin, beige patch that measures about two inches by two inches. It sticks to the skin and is worn on the buttocks, abdomen, upper torso, or upper/outer arm. The patch contains a week's worth of hormones. It's changed once a week for three weeks. On the fourth week, no patch is worn to allow for a monthly period. *Nuva Ring* is a small, flexible ring which is inserted into the vagina. It remains in place for three weeks and is removed on the fourth week to allow for the monthly period. Both of these contraceptives release both estrogen and progestin into the bloodstream to prevent ovulation and thicken the cervical mucus. Advantages and disadvantages of these methods are similar to those of oral contraceptives.

Implanon is a thin, progestin-containing rod which is about the size of a cardboard matchstick and is implanted under the skin of a woman's upper arm. It works in much the same way as the combination birth control pill (preventing ovulation and thickening the cervical mucus). Once implanted, it provides continuous, highly effective contraceptive protection for up to three years. The contraceptive effect is in place within 24 hours and the failure rate is a very impressive 0.05% (Hatcher et al., 2008), meaning that only one in 2000 women using Implanon will become pregnant over the course of a year.

WORKSHEET #50 (CONTINUED)

Depo-Provera is an injection given every three months in the arm or the buttock. It contains only progestin, and prevents pregnancy by thickening the cervical mucus and by preventing ovulation and implantation. Like oral contraceptives, Depo-Provera is highly effective. Unlike oral contraceptives, users do not have to remember to take a pill on a daily basis. Because it contains no estrogen, women who cannot take combination oral contraceptives can use it and it may be used while breast-feeding. The most common side effect associated with Depo-Provera is irregular bleeding. Periods become fewer and lighter with Depo-Provera. After a year of use, half of all women using Depo-Provera will stop having their periods entirely. A weight gain of four to five pounds per year for about three years has been associated with its use. Other side effects are similar to those of oral contraceptives. If a woman experiences negative side effects, she cannot immediately discontinue use, since the drug remains in her system for up to 16 weeks.

Forty-three percent of women who use Depo-Provera discontinue its use, usually because of side effects (Mosher & Jones, 2010). For some women, it may take as long as 18 months for fertility to return after discontinuing Depo-Provera. The median time for conception in women wishing to conceive after discontinuing Depo-Provera is 10 months (Connell, 2002).

WORKSHEET #51

Barrier Methods

Diaphragms and *cervical caps* are latex rubber barriers that cover the cervix so that sperm may not enter the uterus. Both are designed to be used with a spermicide applied to the inner dome. Both may be inserted up to two hours before intercourse and must be left in place for at least eight hours afterward (but not more than 24 hours). Diaphragms and cervical caps need to be fitted by a healthcare professional and refitted if a woman's weight changes by more than ten pounds.

A relatively new type of diaphragm, Lea's Shield, was approved in 2002. It is a one size fits all device used much the same way as a traditional diaphragm, but does not have to be fitted by a health professional.

The *contraceptive sponge* is a soft, disposable sponge which is infused with spermicide and acts as a physical barrier to sperm entering the uterus. It is sold over-the-counter. To use it, a woman moistens the sponge with water and inserts it into the vagina. One sponge provides protection from pregnancy for 24 hours regardless of frequency of intercourse. It must be left in place for six hours after intercourse. By themselves, the diaphragm, the cervical cap, and the contraceptive sponge are not as effective in preventing pregnancy as some other methods; however, they provide a method of contraception that may be used as needed.

Spermicides are agents that kill sperm. Spermicides are available without a prescription in many forms, including foams, jellies, creams, foaming tablets, and vaginal suppositories. For maximum effectiveness, the spermicide should be applied no more than 60 minutes before intercourse and left in place for six to eight hours afterward.

The active ingredient in spermicides available in the United States is Nonoxynol-9. It was once thought that spermicides provided protection from infections such as HIV. Studies have shown that not only is this incorrect, but that nonoxynol-9 may even increase a woman's risk of contracting HIV by causing irritation of the cervix and vagina which may make it easier for viruses to enter the bloodstream (Roody, Zekeng, Ryan, Tamoufe, & Tweedy, 2002).

The *male condom* is a sheath, usually made of latex or polyurethane, that fits over the penis to prevent sperm or microorganisms from entering the vagina or anus. Other than surgical sterilization and withdrawal, condoms are the only form of birth control available to males. Some condoms have a reservoir at the tip to serve as a receptacle for semen. Some have a spermicidal lubricant added, however there is no medical evidence that condoms with spermicide are more effective.

WORKSHEET #51 (CONTINUED)

When condoms are used consistently and correctly for vaginal intercourse, they are effective in preventing pregnancy. With perfect use, condoms have a three percent failure rate. If a hundred couples have intercourse an average of twice each week for a year and use condoms correctly each time, only three of the couples will experience a pregnancy. That means that for that group of a hundred couples, 10,400 condoms were used in the year and only three pregnancies occurred. However, the pregnancy rate for condoms in the way couples typically use them is four times greater than for perfect use. Common mistakes people make when using condoms include: failing to use a condom, putting on the condom too late, and putting it on incorrectly (Hock, 2010).

WORKSHEET #52

Intrauterine Devices (IUDs)

Utilized by nearly 128 million women worldwide, IUDs are the world's most popular form of reversible birth control used by women (Connell, 2002). Although they are becoming more popular, IUDs are much less widely used in the U. S. The two types of IUDs currently available in the United States are the progestin slow-release IUD, Mirena and the T-shaped copper-based Paragard Copper T380A. While Mirena is effective for up to five years, the Copper-T is effective for up to ten years before it needs to be removed or replaced.

IUDs work by preventing fertilization. The presence of the IUD in the uterus causes a mild inflammation and the production of white blood cells which are toxic to sperm and eggs. The Paragard hinders fertilization by inhibiting the transport of sperm through the fallopian tubes, lessening their ability to penetrate the egg, and may even, itself, be toxic to egg and sperm. The progestin in Mirena thickens cervical mucus, thins the inner lining of the uterus, and prevents ovulation. Failure rates associated with IUDs are typically less than one percent per year. Most failures occur within the first year of insertion, particularly in the first three months. In the first year of use, the most common side effects are excessive menstrual cramping and heavier than usual menstrual bleeding. A concern in women who use the IUD is the possible increased risk of pelvic inflammatory disease (PID).

A string that hangs from the IUD through the cervix lets her know that her IUD is in place. Approximately four to five percent of IUDs are expelled during the first year of use. It is most likely to be expelled during menstruation. The progestin in Mirena may help to reduce the uterine contractions that can lead to expulsions. A woman using an IUD should check the string after each menstrual period to make sure that it is still in place.

Commonly Asked Questions
1. Is the IUD expensive?

Answer: _____

_____

_____

_____

_____

WORKSHEET #52 (CONTINUED)

2. Are there any risks associated with the insertion of an IUD?

   Answer: _____

   _____

   _____

   _____

   _____

3. Are there any situations in which a woman should not use an IUD as her form of contraception?

   Answer: _____

   _____

   _____

   _____

   _____

4. Are IUD users at increased risk for problems in pregnancy?

   Answer: _____

   _____

   _____

   _____

   _____

WORKSHEET #53

Fertility Awareness-Based Methods

Fertility awareness-based methods (FABM) of contraception are based on the knowledge that the ability to become pregnant varies during a woman's menstrual cycle. Typically, a woman's fertile days are about five days before ovulation and two days after ovulation, between days 10 and 17 of her cycle. Though these numbers are typical, they may vary from month to month and from woman to woman.

The *calendar (or rhythm) method* of birth control relies on consistency of ovulation during a woman's cycle. For this method, a woman uses a calendar to chart the length of her menstrual cycles. Based on her 12 previous menstrual cycles, a woman subtracts 18 days from her shortest cycle to determine her first fertile day and 11 days from her longest cycle to determine her last fertile day. She would then remain abstinent during this most fertile time. This method is less effective for women with irregular cycles.

With the *basal body temperature (BBT) method* a woman takes her temperature each morning immediately after waking. Prior to ovulation, there may be a slight dip in her temperature. On the day of ovulation, her body temperature generally rises between 0.4 and 0.8°F. It will remain elevated until her period begins. Women using the BBT method should be aware that several factors can influence body temperature including illness, lack of sleep, and alcohol use.

The *cervical mucus method* of birth control involves noting changes in the color and consistency of cervical mucus. Right after menstruation, the vagina feels dry. In the days before ovulation the mucus becomes cloudy and thick. At ovulation, the mucus becomes clear and slippery.

A more expensive option involves the use of an *ovulation predictor kit*, which allows a woman to test her urine daily for the presence of luteinizing hormone which increases 12 to 24 hours prior to ovulation.

WORKSHEET #54

Surgical Methods

A surgical procedure that makes an individual incapable of conceiving or of fertilizing a partner is referred to as ***sterilization*** or ***voluntary surgical contraception (VSC).*** VSC is the most popular method of contraception in the United States, currently used by more than 13 million men and women. The sterilization procedure for a woman is called ***tubal sterilization*** and for a man, ***vasectomy***. Though performed far less often, vasectomies are simpler, more effective, less expensive, and safer procedures then tubal sterilizations.

More than 10 million women in the United States have undergone tubal sterilization. The procedure involves cutting or blocking the fallopian tubes, preventing the egg and sperm from meeting. Eggs are still produced, but they are reabsorbed back into the body.

Typically, between four and five out of every thousand women who have been sterilized may get pregnant because of an ineffective surgical procedure (Pollack, Carignan & Jacobstein, 2004). However, usually while the tiny sperm may be able to reach the egg, the fertilized egg is too large to get past the site where the tube has been cut. It will most likely implant in the fallopian tube, leading to an ectopic pregnancy.

About 500,000 vasectomies are performed in the United States each year. In a vasectomy, the vas deferens, which carry sperm out of the testes, are cut. The man will still produce sperm, but they will be harmlessly reabsorbed into the body. Because sperm contributed about 1 to 5% of the volume of semen, there is no noticeable difference in the amount of ejaculate.

Vasectomy is a simple, outpatient procedure that usually takes between 10 and 20 minutes. A local anesthetic is applied. Vasectomies are about 99.9% successful. The few failures usually occur because the couple has had sex too soon following the procedure and sperm still remain in the reproductive tract. Men are usually advised to wait for 12 weeks or to have 15 to 20 ejaculations to eliminate all of the sperm that remain in the system following the vasectomy.

WORKSHEET #55

Emergency Contraception

Emergency contraception (EC) can be provided by the insertion of a **copper IUD** or by the administration of hormone pills. If inserted within five to seven days after unprotected intercourse, the copper IUD is 99% effective in preventing a pregnancy. The IUD may be left in place for continued contraception or removed after the next menstrual period.

Hormone pills are the most commonly used method. Emergency contraceptive pills contain higher doses of the same hormones found in birth control pills. Combination pills, which contain estrogen and progesterone, are 95% effective in preventing pregnancy when taken within 24 hours after intercourse. If taken within 72 hours they are 75% effective

Plan B, which consists of two doses of progestin, is most effective if taken within 72 hours of unprotected intercourse. It is generally recommended that the first pill be taken as soon as possible after unprotected intercourse and the second dose 12 hours later. The World Health Organization (WHO) suggests taking both Plan B tablets at the same time.

Ella, which acts on progesterone receptors, was approved by the FDA in 2010. Although Ella can be taken within five days of unprotected intercourse, all forms of emergency contraception are most effective when taken as soon as possible.

The hormone treatments work primarily by inhibiting ovulation, thickening cervical mucus, interfering with the transport of sperm through the fallopian tube, or directly affecting the ability of the sperm to fertilize the egg. If fertilization has already occurred, ECPs do not interfere with implantation in the uterus.

Emergency contraception is safe and effective. When Plan B became available without a prescription, for women aged 17 and older, an increasing number of American women used emergency contraception at least once (Mosher & Jones, 2010).

In 2013, a federal judge lifted the age restriction, ruling that emergency contraception products must be sold without a prescription or other restrictions to women of all ages (NPR, 2013). In spite of the federal ruling, as of this writing the Food and Drug Administration has elected to make the product available over-the-counter to those aged 15 and older.

WORKSHEET #56

Common Myths About Contraception

1. A woman can't get pregnant having sex during her period.

    _____

    _____

2. Breast-feeding her baby protects a woman from pregnancy.

    _____

    _____

3. If a man withdraws his penis before he ejaculates, his partner won't get pregnant.

    _____

    _____

4. Using vaginal douches or taking a hot bath after sex can prevent pregnancy.

    _____

    _____

5. The female can't get pregnant if it's the first time she's having sex.

    _____

    _____

6. Even if a woman still gets her period, she may be too old to get pregnant.

    _____

    _____

WORKSHEET #57

Counseling About Contraception

You are health counselor at the local family planning center. During the course of the day, you encounter the following clients:

1. **Bonnie**
   Bonnie is a 24-year-old single woman who has multiple sexual partners. She wants to know your opinion about what type of birth control would be the best choice for her.

   Your Answer: _____

   _____

   _____

   _____

   _____

   _____

2. **Mitch**
   Mitch is a 38-year-old married man who had a vasectomy yesterday. He wants to know if he can begin to have unprotected sex with his wife right away.

   Your Answer: _____

   _____

   _____

   _____

   _____

   _____

WORKSHEET #57 (CONTINUED)

3. **Cindy**

Cindy wants to know if emergency contraception is a form of abortion.

Your Answer: _____

_____

_____

_____

_____

_____

_____

4. **Lyn**

Lyn wants to use an effective hormonal method of birth control, but she often forgets to take the birth control pill. She wants to know what other method might better suit her.

Your Answer: _____

_____

_____

_____

_____

_____

_____

WORKSHEET #57 (CONTINUED)

5. **Marie**

Because of Marie's religious beliefs, she and her husband want to practice the rhythm method of birth control. Marie wants to know how to figure out when she and her husband should remain abstinent.

Your Answer: _____

_____

_____

_____

_____

_____

_____

WORKSHEET #58

NAME _____

Contraceptive Match

A. Combination oral
    contraceptive

B. Vasectomy

C. Depo provera

D. Spermicides

E. Male condom

F. Diaphragm

G. Ortho evra

H. Contraceptive sponge

I. IUD

J. Plan B

_____1. Thin patch which contains a week's worth of hormones

_____2. Latex rubber barrier that covers the cervix

_____3. World's most popular form of reversible birth control

_____4. Outpatient surgical procedure for men

_____5. One pill taken each day for 21 days

_____6. Foams, jellies, or other sperm killing agents

_____7. Latex sheath that fits over the penis

_____8. Injection given every 3 months

_____9. Most effective if taken within 72 hours of unprotected
intercourse

_____10. Moistened with water before inserted into the vagina

PART VII: READING

Abortion and Fetal Abnormalities

Testing for fetal abnormalities can alert expectant parents to potential health problems to come.

Prenatal testing includes screening tests and diagnostic tests. Screening tests can identify whether the baby is at risk to have certain conditions – but they usually can't result in a definite diagnosis. Screening tests, such as ultrasound and blood tests, are a routine part of prenatal care and pose no risk to the mother or the fetus.

If the screening test indicates a possible problem – or if maternal age or family history or medical history puts the couple at increased risk of having a baby with a health problem, they and their doctor might consider additional diagnostic tests. Some diagnostic tests, such as chorionic villus sampling (CVS) or amniocentesis carry a very slight risk of miscarriage. CVS, which can test for chromosomal abnormalities and some other genetic problems, is usually performed between the 10th and 12th week of pregnancy.

Amniocentesis, which can also test for chromosomal abnormalities as well as neural tube defects, such as spina bifida, is generally offered between the 15th and 20th week of pregnancy.

Dave and Allison met in college. They got along great right from the start. After graduation, they married. Allison began her career as a high school English teacher while in graduate school. They rented a small apartment, saved every cent they could and were very happy together.

Five years passed. Allison had become an assistant principal and Dave, along with a partner, had opened a small restaurant which was becoming a fast hit. Life was perfect except for one thing – a baby. They wanted a child very badly. Finally, after three years of trying, Allison became pregnant.

Allison was seeing an obstetrician who was very highly regarded and who she liked very much. In her second trimester the doctor ordered a typical screening test – an alpha fetoprotein screening (AFP). This is a blood test that measures the level of AFP in the mother's blood during pregnancy. AFP is a protein normally produced by the fetal liver. It is present in the fluid surrounding the fetus (amniotic fluid) and crosses the placenta into the mother's blood. Abnormal levels of AFP may signal a number of problems – one of which being the neural tube defect, spina bifida.

PART VII: READING (CONTINUED)

Spina bifida is a birth defect which appears in 1 to 2 live births per 1000 worldwide. In spina bifida, the bones of the spine do not close around the spinal cord as they should during fetal development. Normally, the neural tube closes at 3 to 4 weeks after conception. There are several types of spina bifida, which range from mild to severe. While the mildest form often causes no symptoms or disability, the most severe form can result in complications such as complete motor paralysis (unable to walk) and severe mental disabilities. It depends on variables such as the size and location of the malformation and which spinal nerves are involved.

When Allison's blood tests showed abnormal levels of AFP, the doctor ordered several additional tests – an ultrasound was performed as was an amniocentesis.

The doctor told Dave and Allison that, although the test could not reveal the severity of the defect, the amniocentesis indicated that their baby would be born with spina bifida. Dave and Allison were stunned. Soon after learning the news, they began to anguish over what to do. Did they want to have the baby that they had wanted for so long or should Allison have an abortion rather than to have a child who may be severely disabled?

At this writing, the governor of North Dakota is considering signing two anti-abortion bills that would be the most restrictive in the nation.

The bills would prohibit abortion after six weeks and ban them for reasons of fetal abnormalities. If signed, the bills would take the decision out of the hands of the parents.

The fetal abnormalities bill would ban abortions due to any defect, disease, or disorder that is genetic – and the ban extends to physical disfigurement. Basically, it means that women in North Dakota who are told that they're carrying a fetus with Down Syndrome, spina bifida, or fatal conditions such as anencephaly (a condition in which the brain does not form) will no longer be able to legally end their pregnancies.

NAME _____

1. *Does the parental right to choose override the fetus' is right to live? Explain.*

_____

_____

_____

_____

_____

_____

_____

_____

2. *Should abortion on the grounds of fetal abnormalities be banned? Explain.*

_____

_____

_____

_____

_____

_____

_____

_____

REFERENCES

Connell, E.B. (2002). *The contraception sourcebook*. New York: Contemporary Books.

Hatcher, R.A., Trussel, J., Nelson, A., Cates, W., Stewart, F., and Kowal, D. (2008). *Contraceptive technology*, (19th rev. ed.) New York: Ardent Media.

Hock, R.R. (2010). *Human sexuality*, (2nd ed.) Upper Saddle River: Prentice Hall.

McCarthy, L. and Brar, H. (2008). Levonorgestrel/ethinyl estradiol (Lybrel) for continuous contraception. *American Family Physician, 77*, 222-223.

Mosher, W.D. and Jones, J. (2010). Use of contraception in the U.S.: 1982-2008. Data from The National Survey of Family Growth. Vital and Health Statistics, Series 23(29). Hyattsville, MD: National Center for Health Statistics.

National Public Radio. *With Plan B Ruling, Judge Signs off on Years of Advocacy*. April 2013. *NPR*. Web 7 April 2013. <www.npr.org/blogs/health/2013/04/05/176396151/ with-plan-b-ruling-judge-signs-off-on-years-of-advocacy>

Pollack, A.E., Carignan, C.S., and Jacobstein, R. (2004). Female and male sterilization. In R.A. Hatcher, J. Trussell, F. Stewart, A. Nelson, W. Cates, F. Guest, and D. Kowal (Eds.) *Contemporary technology* (18th ed.), New York: Ardent Media, 531-574.

Roody, R.E., Zekeng, L., Ryan, K.A. Tamoufe, U., and Tweedy, K.G. (2002). Effect of nonoxynol-9 on urogenital gonorrhea and chlamydial infection: a randomized controlled trial. *Journal of the American Medical Association, 287*(9), 1117-1122.

Sulak, P. (2007). The demise of 21/7 contraceptive regimens. *Family Practice News, 87*, 9.

PART VIII

PREGNANCY

WORKSHEET #59

Conception

Following ovulation, the ovum can live for up to 24 hours. The majority of sperm live up to 72 hours in the female reproductive tract. Although most sperm die within 72 hours, a small number may survive for five to seven days.

Conception is the fertilization of an egg by a sperm. It typically occurs in the fallopian tube. During intercourse, sperm are ejaculated into the vagina. They travel through the cervix and uterus into the fallopian tube.

Though the average ejaculation contains several hundred million sperm, fewer than 200 typically reach a fallopian tube and even fewer reach the recently released ovum, or egg cell. Several sperm may reach the ovum, but only one may fertilize it.

The sperm secretes a chemical that bores a hole through the outer layer of the ovum and allows the sperm to penetrate. The ovum immediately undergoes a physical change so that it is impossible for any other sperm to enter. An egg fertilized by more than one sperm would be spontaneously aborted.

Once the sperm enters the egg, its body and tail detach and its nucleus is drawn toward the nucleus of the egg, where the chromosomes combine. Each sperm contains 23 chromosomes, including the X or Y sex chromosome which determines whether the fetus is male or female (the egg also contributes 23 for a total of 46 chromosomes).

Approximately 12 hours after the genetic material from the sperm and egg join, cell division begins. The collection of cells is called a blastocyst. About three to four days after conception, the blastocyst enters the uterus. Implantation of the developing embryo usually occurs five to eight days after fertilization (from the second through the eighth weeks, the developing human is called an embryo).

At the beginning of the third week, the placenta begins to develop. The placenta is the structure through which nutrients, blood gases, and wastes are exchanged between maternal and fetal blood. The placenta is connected to the fetus by the umbilical cord.

In addition, a membrane called the amniotic sac begins to grow over the developing embryo and the cavity fills with fluid which supports and protects the embryo, and later, the fetus.

WORKSHEET #60

Tests to Confirm Pregnancy and Early Signs of Pregnancy

A woman produces a hormone called human chorionic gonadotropin (hCG) when a fertilized egg implants in her uterus. It is produced in the placenta very early in the pregnancy. The presence of hCG helps to build and maintain a thick endometrial layer and prevent menstruation.

Home pregnancy tests determine the hCG level in a woman's urine. The levels begin to rise seven to nine days after fertilization. It can first be detected by a blood test about 11 days after conception and by a urine test 12 to 14 days after conception.

The most common early indicator of pregnancy is a missed period although some women experience "spotting" during the pregnancy (more bleeding is not to be expected and is a sign of a possible miscarriage). Other physical signs include breast tenderness and morning sickness which, if it occurs at all, most commonly appears early in the pregnancy.

Even though it is called "morning" sickness, nausea and vomiting can occur at any time. It is due to fluctuations in hormone levels during pregnancy, which may irritate the stomach lining.

Some research suggests that morning sickness may protect the fetus from food-borne illness and unhealthy additives in some foods during the first trimester, since it is a critical time in development (Boyd, 2000).

A far less common occurrence is pseudoscyesis, more often known as false pregnancy. This is a condition in which a woman believes that she is pregnant though she is not. She will experience several signs of pregnancy, such as missed periods, morning sickness, and weight gain. Most of these cases have a psychological cause, though at times, the cause is physical. A tumor on the pituitary gland, for example, can cause symptoms such as breast tenderness, nausea, and vomiting.

WORKSHEET #61

Development of the Embryo and Fetus

First Trimester (first three months of pregnancy)

From the time it implants in the uterus until eight weeks after fertilization, the fertilized egg is called an embryo. During this time period, the major organs begin to develop and the placenta and umbilical cord are formed. Though each day about ten percent of the mother's total blood flow passes through the placenta, the blood supply of the mother and the fetus do not mix. The placenta allows certain substances to get through to the fetus while it prevents others. Unfortunately, in addition to oxygen, glucose, and other nutrients, as well as other beneficial materials, things like alcohol, nicotine, and most other drugs can cross into the blood supply of the fetus.

The heart is one of the first organs to develop because it is needed to carry oxygen and other nutrients to rapidly developing tissues. By the end of the first month, the heart begins to pump blood. The eyes, brain, and spinal cord begin to develop as do the beginning of arm and leg buds. Sexual differentiation begins with the development of testes or ovaries.

Beginning with the start of week nine through birth, the developing baby is known as a fetus. By the end of the first trimester, the circulatory and urinary systems are operating and the fetus weighs approximately .5 ounce and is approximately 3 inches long.

Second Trimester (middle three months of pregnancy)

During the second trimester, the fetus grows dramatically. By the end of the second trimester, the fetus may be a little over one foot long and weigh about two pounds.

The fetus develops reflexes, such as sucking and swallowing. Bone begins to develop, although joints are not yet formed. The developing fetus may begin to kick and move, and by the middle of the second trimester, responds to sound.

During the second trimester, the fetal body is covered with soft, fine hair, called lanugo, and a waxy substance, called vernix. It is thought that the greasy vernix protects the fetus from its immersion in amniotic fluid and lubricates it during delivery.

There is a possibility that a baby born at the end of the second trimester could survive.

WORKSHEET #61 (CONTINUED)

Third Trimester (last three months of pregnancy)

During the last three months of pregnancy, the fetus greatly increases in size. By the end of the seventh month, the fetus develops fat deposits; the head and the body become more proportionate; and all organ systems continue to develop. Though they are still immature, the lungs are beginning to function. During the eighth month, the fetus may weigh four to six pounds. The fetus can react to light and sounds and may begin to suck its thumb.

By the beginning of the ninth month, there is less fetal movement because the fetus has less room in which to move. At birth, the average infant weighs 7.5 pounds and is 20 inches long.

WORKSHEET #62

Problems During Pregnancy

Ectopic Pregnancy

In an ectopic pregnancy, the zygote implants outside of the uterus (almost always in the fallopian tube). About one in 50 pregnancies in the United States are ectopic. The number has been increasing, mostly due to the increase in the incidence of pelvic inflammatory disease caused by untreated chlamydial infections. Symptoms may include abdominal pain, cramping, vaginal bleeding, and nausea.

Though many women without risk factors can experience an ectopic pregnancy certain risk factors put a woman at increased risk. Women who smoke and those who have a sexually transmitted infection are at increased risk of having an ectopic pregnancy.

Nowadays, through diagnostic tools such as ultrasound, ectopic pregnancies can often be discovered and treated without surgical intervention.

Miscarriage

A miscarriage, or spontaneous abortion, is the natural termination of a pregnancy before the time the embryo or fetus can live outside of the uterus. Most miscarriages occur during the first trimester and are often caused by a chromosomal abnormality (Vorsanova et al., 2010).

In situations where there is no chromosomal abnormality, miscarriage may be the result of abnormal conditions of the cervix, uterus, or placenta, nutritional deficiencies, exposure to toxic substances, or even extreme stress.

While the physical effects of a miscarriage are not usually severe, the experience can be emotionally devastating to a woman and her partner. Although it can be very difficult for both, research has found that women experience more intense emotional symptoms for a longer period of time than their male partners (Musters et al., 2011).

Birth Defects

The March of Dimes estimates that one of every 33 babies is born with a birth defect and birth defects cause one in five infant deaths. Prenatal diagnostic testing can be used to determine whether there is a genetic or chromosomal abnormality in the fetus.

WORKSHEET #63

Teratogens

Many substances including some that would be considered relatively harmless under other circumstances, are potentially extremely harmful during pregnancy. They are ***teratogens***, substances which are capable of crossing the placenta, entering the bloodstream of the fetus, and causing physical or mental deficiencies.

Examples of Teratogens:

1. ***Marijuana***

   After delivery, some babies who were regularly exposed to marijuana before birth appear to have withdrawal-like symptoms, including excessive crying and trembling. These babies are more sensitive to stimulation and have poor sleep patterns. Research suggests that children who were exposed to marijuana before birth are more likely to have subtle problems that affect their ability to pay attention (National Institute on Drug Abuse, 2012).

   Your friend smokes marijuana several times a week. The woman doesn't plan to continue smoking during her pregnancy. The couple assumes that it doesn't matter how much marijuana they smoke before the pregnancy. Are they correct?

   _____

   _____

2. ***Ecstasy, Methamphetamine and Other Amphetamines***

   The use of these drugs has increased significantly in recent years, so there have been few studies of their effect on pregnancy. Limited research has found a possible increase in congenital heart defects. Ecstasy, as well as amphetamines, are associated with low birth weight and smaller than normal head circumference. There's also an increased risk of complications during the pregnancy, such as premature birth. After delivery, some babies exposed to amphetamines appear to have withdrawal-like symptoms including jitteriness and breathing problems.

   Someone you know used crystal meth during her pregnancy. She wonders if her baby could experience any long-term effects as a result. What do you tell her?

   _____

   _____

WORKSHEET #63 (CONTINUED)

3. *Heroin*

Women who use heroin during pregnancy greatly increase the risk of serious pregnancy complications. These risks include poor fetal growth, premature rupture of the amniotic sac, premature birth, and *stillbirth* (fetus delivered after 20 weeks of gestation).

As many as half of all babies of heroin users are born with low birthweight (Briggs et al., 2005). Many of these babies are premature and often suffer from serious health problems during the newborn period, including respiratory problems. They also are at increased risk of lifelong disabilities.

Most babies of heroin users show withdrawal symptoms during the three days after birth, including fever, trembling, diarrhea, vomiting, and seizures. These symptoms may subside after about a week or continue for several weeks. The severity of a baby's symptoms is related to how long the mother has been using heroin or other narcotics. Babies exposed to heroin before birth also face an increased risk of *sudden infant death syndrome* (SIDS).

4. *Cocaine*

Cocaine exposed babies are more likely than unexposed babies to be born prematurely and with low birth weight. Premature and low birth weight babies are at increased risk of health problems during the newborn period, lasting disabilities such as intellectual disabilities, and cerebral palsy. Cocaine exposed babies also tend to have smaller heads, which generally reflect smaller brains and an increased risk of learning problems (Bateman & Chiriboga, 2000). There is also an increased risk of SIDS among babies whose mothers used cocaine while pregnant.

Cocaine may cause the fetus to have a stroke, which can result in irreversible brain damage and sometimes death.

Cocaine use during pregnancy can cause placental problems, including placental abruption. In this condition, the placenta pulls away from the wall of the uterus before labor begins. This can lead to heavy bleeding that can be life-threatening for both mother and baby. The baby may be deprived of oxygen and adequate blood flow when an abruption occurs. Prompt cesarean delivery can prevent most deaths but may not prevent serious complications for the baby caused by lack of oxygen (Bauer et al., 2005).

WORKSHEET #63 (CONTINUED)

5. *Nicotine*

Nicotine is a powerful blood vessel constrictor. As such, if a woman smokes cigarettes while pregnant, the flow of oxygen and nutrients to the fetus may be significantly reduced. This results in an increased risk of complications during pregnancy, miscarriage, premature birth, low birth weight, and increased incidence of SIDS.

Smoking has been linked to 115,000 miscarriages and 5,600 infant deaths a year (Murkoff et al., 2002).

WORKSHEET #64

Fetal Alcohol Spectrum Disorders

What are fetal alcohol spectrum disorders?

Fetal alcohol spectrum disorders (FASDs) is the name given to a group of conditions that a person can have if that person's mother drank alcohol while she was pregnant. These conditions include physical and intellectual disabilities, as well as problems with behavior and learning. Often, a person has a combination of these problems. FASDs are a leading known cause of intellectual disability and birth defects.

1. Is there an amount of alcohol that is safe to drink while pregnant?

_____

_____

_____

2. Is it safe to drink once the first trimester has passed?

_____

_____

_____

3. What are some signs of FASDs?

_____

_____

_____

4. Can FASDs be prevented?

_____

_____

_____

WORSHEET #65

Abortion

1973 Roe v. Wade
Supreme court decision
Decided that they are legal — rules vary between states

1. What is meant by a "back-alley abortion?"

2. How long has abortion been legal in the U.S.? Does legalization mean that a woman can have an abortion at any time during the pregnancy?

3. Does a fetus have legal rights?

NO

4. Is it a requirement for minors to get parental consent to have an abortion?

Depends what state you are in

5. What is meant by the term "partial-birth abortion?"

6. What do people mean when they refer to the "abortion pill?"

RU486
Mifipristone) Can be given up to 7 ween.
into preg. for to abort.

7. How common are abortions in the U.S.? Are they safe?

Rsh of Death per million.

abortion 1st trimester - 4
Driving a car 16a
Pro + Driving 100

WORKSHEET #66

NAME _____

Your Position on Abortion

	Agree	Disagree

1. The fertilized egg is a human being from the moment of conception.

2. In cases of teenagers seeking an abortion,
   parental consent should be required.

3. In cases of married women seeking an abortion,
   spousal consent should be required.

4. The federal government should provide public funding for
   abortion to ensure equal access to abortion for all women.

   _____

5. Does a woman's right to choose whether or not to have an abortion depend upon the circumstances surrounding conception or the situation of the mother or father? In which of the following situations, if any, would you support a woman's right to choose to have an abortion?

   _____ An abortion is necessary to maintain the woman's life or health.

   _____ The pregnancy is a result of rape or incest.

   _____ The pregnancy is a result of the failure of a contraceptive method or device.

   _____ The pregnancy occurred when no contraceptive method was in use.

   _____ A couple having their fifth baby feels they cannot support another child.

   _____ A single woman has had three abortions and wants to have her fourth.

   _____ A pregnant 23-year-old law student does not want to interrupt her education.

   _____ The father of the child has stated he will provide no support and does not want the mother or the child to be part of his life.

   _____ Parents of three girls wish to terminate the mother's pregnancy because the fetus is female rather than male.

WORKSHEET #66 (CONTINUED)

Explain why you answered as you did.

_____

_____

_____

_____

_____

_____

_____

_____

_____

_____

_____

_____

_____

_____

_____

_____

_____

_____

_____

PART VIII: READING

The Case of Baby Veronica

In April of 2013, the nine justices of the United States Supreme Court presided over the type of case that normally would have been reserved for Family Court. The emotionally charged case centers around the custody of an adorable 3 1/2-year-old little girl named Veronica.

In 2010, Dustin Brown and his girlfriend, Christina Maldonado found out that Christina was pregnant. Brown wanted to get married. Maldonado resisted and they separated. Brown, who was in the U.S. Army, was stationed in a town a few hours away from the town in Oklahoma where Maldonado was living. He informed Maldonado that he would rather give up parental rights then pay child support. Brown signed legal papers stating that he would not contest the adoption of the baby girl and that he waived the 30 day waiting period and notice of the hearing. He believed that he was relinquishing rights to Maldonado.

A few months prior to the baby's birth, Maldonado worked with an adoption attorney to place Veronica with Matt and Melanie Capobianco, who lived in South Carolina. When Brown realized that he had signed away his rights to adoptive parents rather than to his ex-girlfriend, he contested the adoption. A series of court rulings eventually brought the case to the U.S. Supreme Court which was asked to decide who gets to keep baby Veronica – the adoptive couple who raised her for 27 months or the biological father to whom the South Carolina state court granted custody. The reason this case was heard by the Supreme Court is its unusual circumstances: Dustin Brown is a member of the Cherokee Nation. Veronica is $3/256^{th}$ Cherokee. In 1978, Congress passed the Indian Child Welfare Act to prevent the involuntary break up of Native American families. Given their involvement during the pregnancy, birth, and early years of Veronica's life versus the father's absence, state courts would likely decide in favor of the adoptive parents. Instead, the state court in South Carolina gave the edge to the biological father because of the federal law involved.

During the oral arguments before the Supreme Court Justice, Antonin Scalia, who is the father of nine children, and Chief Justice John Roberts, whose two children are adopted, sat side-by-side – but were miles apart emotionally. Justice Scalia said, "This guy (Brown) is the father of the child, and they're taking the child away from him even though he wants it." Scalia said that whether the adoptive parents would make better parents is not relevant. "I know a lot of kids that would be better off with different parents," he said.   In contrast, Chief Justice Roberts noted that Brown had not shown any interest in fatherhood nor child support until the court battle began. He said that the federal law gives undue preference to Native American bloodlines, no matter how small. When Brown's attorney said that the father had been "excited" by Maldonado's pregnancy, Roberts responded, "So he was excited by it, he just didn't want to take any responsibility." Attorneys for the couple argued that the law is racially discriminatory – in effect, banning adoptions of Native American children by anyone who's not Native American.

NAME _____

On June 26, 2013, the Supreme Court ruled that the biological father could not rely on the Indian Child Welfare Act to undo Brown's termination of parental rights over his daughter.

Would you have ruled in favor of the biological father or the adoptive parents in this case? In general, what factors influence your opinion when it comes to cases where biological parent(s) seek to regain custody of the child after the child is living with adoptive parent(s)?

_____

_____

_____

_____

_____

_____

_____

_____

_____

_____

_____

_____

_____

_____

_____

_____

_____

_____

REFERENCES

Bateman, D.A. and Chiriboga, C.A. (2000). Dose-responsive effect of cocaine on newborn head circumference. *Pediatrics*, 106(3), e33.

Bauer, C.R., et al. (2005). Acute neonatal effects of cocaine exposure during pregnancy. *Archives of Pediatric and Adolescent Medicine*, 159, 824-834.

Boyd, L. (2000). Morning sickness shields fetus from bugs and chemicals. *RN*, 63(3). 18-20.

Briggs, G.G., et al. (2005). *Drugs in Pregnancy and Lactation* (2nd ed.). Philadelphia: Lippincott Williams and Wilkins.

Murkoff, H.E., Eisenberg, A., and Hathaway, S.E. (2002). *What to Expect When You're Expecting*. New York: Workman Publishing.

Musters, A.M., Taminiau-Bloem, E.F., VandenBoogaard, E., Vanderveen, F., and Goddijn, M. (2011). Supportive care for women with unexplained recurrent miscarriage: patients' Perspectives, *Human Reproduction*, 26(4) 873-877.

National Institute on Drug Abuse. *Research Report Series – Marijuana Abuse*. Updated July 2012.

Tay J.E., Moore, J., and Walker, J.J. (2000). Ectopic pregnancy. *British Medical Journal*, 320(7239), 916-920.

Vorsanova, S., et al. (2010). Chromosomal mosaicism in spontaneous abortions: analysis of 650 cases. *Genetika*, 46(10), 1356-1359.

PART IX

GENDER ISSUES

WORKSHEET #67

Development of Biological Sex

Most cells in the body contains 46 chromosomes: 23 from the mother and 23 from the father. Twenty-two of the pairs look practically identical. The 23rd pair, the sex chromosomes, determine whether a person is male or female. The two sex chromosomes are made up of an X chromosome donated by the mother and either an X or a Y chromosome donated by the father.

During the first six weeks of prenatal development, the gonads and genitalia of embryos are identical. Embryos have two duct systems: the Müllerian (which will become the female reproductive anatomy) and the Wolffian (which will become the male reproductive anatomy).

By week eight of prenatal development, the sex chromosomes will begin to influence the anatomical and hormonal development of the embryo. By the end of week 12, genitalia have been differentiated and may be identified as male or female.

Disorders of Sex Development/InterSexuality

At any stage of prenatal development, a disorder of sex development can occur. Although dozens of such conditions exist, only a few will be described in this chapter.

Many people inaccurately use the term "hermaphrodite" to describe someone with DSD. A true hermaphrodite (a term which is no longer used) is born with both testes and ovaries. The person may have an ovary and fallopian tube on one side of the body and testicles and vas deferens on the other side. This condition is quite rare.

More commonly, an individual has the gonads of their chromosomal sex and ambiguous genitalia (a combination of male and female reproductive anatomy) or external genitalia that is the opposite of their chromosomal sex. While this used to be called pseudohermaphroditism, it is now known as disorders of sex development (DSD) or intersex. In approximately one out of every 4,500 births, the genitalia is so ambiguous that the newborn's sex is not able to be determined (Diamond, 2005).

Klinefelter Syndrome

This occurs when an ovum containing an extra X chromosome is fertilized by a Y chromosome (XXY), giving the boy 47 chromosomes. While the Y chromosome triggers the development of male genitalia, the extra X prevents them from developing completely.

WORKSHEET #67 (CONTINUED)

As adults, men with Klinefelter syndrome have small testes, low levels of testosterone, and gynecomastia (breast development in males). The influence of the extra X chromosome also results in a feminine body shape, decreased muscle mass, and sparse body hair. Males with Klinefelter syndrome have reduced sex drive, erectile difficulties, and infertility problems. It is also associated with developmental problems (reading, writing, speech, and problem solving difficulties).

Treatment is testosterone therapy. If begun during adolescence, it can enhance the development of secondary sex characteristics and may help to improve body shape and increase sex drive. This condition occurs in one in every 750 live male births (Forti et al., 2010).

Guevedoces

This is a rare genetic condition in which the infant is born with apparently female genitalia. However, these children are missing the enzyme that converts testosterone to dihydrotestosterone (DHT). They have a Y chromosome, therefore they develop testes and testosterone. This leads to the development of internal male reproductive organs. The testes produce a hormone that prevents the growth of internal female reproductive organs. DHT causes prenatal growth of the penis and descent of the testes into the scrotal sac. Because these children lack this enzyme (DHT) they have a female or ambiguous appearance at birth. Upon puberty, the undescended testes produce enough testosterone to cause what appears to be a clitoris, to grow into a penis, and the labia majora to fuse into a scrotal sac. These children may then adopt a male gender identity or undergo feminizing surgery and hormonal treatment and live as females.

Turner Syndrome

This occurs when an ovum without any X chromosome is fertilized by an X sperm (XO). A child with this syndrome has only 45 chromosomes. It occurs in one of every 2,500 live female births. The female with this condition will not menstruate (amenorrhea). Her breasts will not develop and she will have abnormalities in her female reproductive organs, (i.e. non-functioning ovaries). She will also have abnormally short stature.

The administration of estrogen and progesterone during puberty can help to enhance secondary sex characteristics. Most girls will not go through puberty, but those who do *may* be able to conceive.

WORKSHEET #67 (CONTINUED)

If someone has an intersexed child, one step they should probably take is to learn more about the DSD through consultation with physicians, geneticists, and psychologists who have specialized knowledge in the area.

Most experts believe that surgery should not be performed on an intersexed child simply to have the child conform to societal expectations. Even if the parents aren't comfortable with the fact that the sex of their child is not absolute, the most important question remains: what is best for the child?

- *What challenges would the parents of an intersexed child face?*

- *What challenges would the child face?*

WORKSHEET #68

Differences and Similarities between Males and Females

1. *Physiological*

   There are physical differences in almost every organ of the male and female bodies. Take the brain for example. Parts of the frontal cortex involved in reasoning and decision-making are larger in women, while males have larger parietal lobes (involved in spatial perception).

2. *Behavioral*

   Most people consider males to be more aggressive than females and females to be more emotional than males.

   While some people believe that testosterone causes violent behavior, its effect on human aggression is actually unclear (Simpson, 2001). Potentially, women may be as aggressive as men, but are under more social constraint in the expression of their aggression (Richardson & Hammock, 2007).

   Do females experience more emotions than males? While infant boys are more emotionally expressive than infant girls, boys are socialized throughout their lives to show less emotion (Eliot, 2009). When a baby girl falls down, she is often cuddled and comforted. When a baby boy falls down, he is often told (particularly by males) not to cry and to "act like a man."

3. *Cognitive Differences*

   Research indicates that females excel in verbal abilities, such as reading comprehension, while males excel in spatial tasks (Halpern & LaMay, 2000). While testosterone may improve performance on spatial tasks, it is thought that inborn differences affecting academic achievement are small. The individual's learning environment, expectations of teachers, and self-confidence all play a much more significant role in academic performance.

WORKSHEET #69

Sex, Gender, and Gender Roles

Although the words are often used synonymously, the word sex refers to the biological aspects of being male or female, while gender refers to the behavioral, psychological, and social characteristics of men and women.

So –   The symptoms of heart disease depend on the sex of the individual (not the gender). The preponderance of female nursery school teachers is related to gender roles (not their sex).

There are societal expectations of behavior for each gender. The expectation of behaviors for a particular gender by a society are called **_gender roles_**. Gender roles are reinforced from multiple sources: parents, peers, teachers, the media.

Socialization is the process through which we learn and adopt the behavior patterns of a culture. Socialization into gender roles begins very early.

- Adults tend to play more roughly with little boys and coddle the girls more when they hurt themselves.
- Parents are often more protective of girls and allow boys to have more freedom.
- Children are given toys and placed in activities that are considered gender appropriate. i.e. trucks for boys and dolls for girls.

It may not be that society alone influences gender stereotyping of toys and activities. Children may choose gender-traditional toys before they have a sense of their gender (Hasset, Siebert, & Wallen, 2008). Even so, society significantly impacts children's adoption of gender roles.

It is generally accepted that, by adulthood, our gender roles are firmly established.

WORKSHEET #70

Transgender

Gender identity is one's sense of themselves as being a man or a woman. Gender identity is usually formed by three years of age. In some people, their biological sex does not match their gender identity. These people are called transgender (or transsexual).

A transsexual individual *may* have **gender dysphoria** (also called gender identity disorder). This is a psychological condition in which the mismatch between an individual's biological sex and their gender identity is distressing enough to cause impairment in their daily living. Not all transsexual people have gender dysphoria. Many are comfortable about their biological sex and gender identity.

It used to be thought that gender identity was completely dependent on how boys and girls are brought up. Research now tells us that gender identity is also a product of factors such as brain structure, genetic variations, and prenatal hormone physiology (Kruijver et al., 2000; Hare et al., 2009; Green & Young, 2001).

Gender Transitions

Step 1   Female to male transsexuals are biological females and male to female transsexuals are biological males. Treatment for both begins with psychotherapy. Psychotherapy helps the individual to explore their feelings and their options and to establish their goals.

Step 2   Individuals may next elect to take on the role of the desired gender. Living as the desired gender will help the individual to better understand the effects that changing gender will have on their lives.

Step 3   Some individuals will next elect to undergo extensive hormone therapy. These hormones (androgens given to transmen and estrogens given to transwomen) will lead to significant physical changes. Transwomen, for example, will experience breast development, a redistribution of body fat, a decrease in body hair, and softening of the skin. Transmen will experience increased facial and body hair, increased upper body strength, and clitoral enlargement.

Step 4   Some transsexuals will elect to undergo sexual reassignment surgery. A transwoman's genital surgeries include removal of the penis and testicles and rerouting of the urethra. Transmen's genital surgeries include a hysterectomy and a procedure called a metoidioplasty which releases the enlarged clitoris allowing it to hang like a natural penis. Another surgical option involves constructing an artificial penis from abdominal tissue.

WORKSHEET #70 (CONTINUED)

Some societies embrace different forms of gender expression. Many Native American tribes believe that there are three genders: female, male, and two-spirit. Two-spirits have both masculine and feminine spirits in the same body.

In the United States, transgendered people have faced the loss of their jobs, their homes, even their lives:

Brandon Teena was a transman who was raped and murdered
at the age of 21 when several men learned of his biological sex.

Transgendered individuals have a 1 in 12 chance of being murdered compared to a 1 in 18,000 chance in the general population (Human Rights Campaign, 2009).

1. *Why do some people react to transgendered individuals with such anger and violence?*

2. *Your six-year-old son tells you that he doesn't feel like a boy and that he wants to be a girl. He wants to wear his sister's clothes and play with her dolls. He says that he doesn't want to have a penis. What do you do?*

Note: A *transwoman* is a person who was born male but identifies as a female.

               A *transman* is a person who was born female identified as a male.

               Transgender should not be confused with transvestite. A *transvestite* is someone who is sexually aroused by dressing in the clothes of the opposite sex.

WORKSHEET #71

Gender Inequality in the U.S.: Equal Pay for Equal Work?

In a poll of 9 million households conducted by the U.S. Census Bureau, women earned $.79 for every dollar made by men in the United States. The gender pay gap is independent of occupation, experience, and education (Bloomberg News, 2012).

There was a day, several decades ago, when the most common family situation was a working father and a stay-at-home mother. However, in 2010, U.S. women comprised half of all people in the workforce and 40% of these women were the family's main source of income. In low income families, women are the primary source of income in two out of every three households (Center for American Progress, 2010).

In addition to earning less money for doing the same work as their male counterparts, working women still perform the vast majority of housework (Lachance-Brzela & Bouchard, 2010).

You and your co-worker (same gender) have the same educational background and work experience and you both receive similar, positive evaluations from your employer. One day in a discussion about salaries, you learn that your co-worker makes significantly more money than you.

1. *How would you feel?*

2. *Given all of the similarities between you and your coworker, what reason(s) could account for the pay difference?*

WORKSHEET #72

Gender Inequality Worldwide

The following list highlights examples of gender inequality throughout the world:

Limited Mobility

In Saudi Arabia women are not allowed to drive a car or ride a bicycle on public roads.

Violence

In 2008, the U.N. Secretary-General reported that one in every three women is likely to be beaten, coerced into sex, or otherwise abused in her lifetime. In both the developed and the developing world, violence against women in the form of rape, spousal abuse, child abuse, or spousal killing is such routine behavior that it rarely even makes the news.

Infanticide

In some countries, such as China and India, a male child is much more valuable than a female child. Some parents elect to end a pregnancy that would result in a female child or even kill the child after its birth.

Restricted Land Ownership

In some countries, such as Chile, women lack the right to own land. All deeds must include the name of a man (her husband or father). If he dies, the woman has no legal claim to land she may have lived and worked on all of her life.

Education

Women make up more than 2/3 of the world's illiterate adults. Girls may be kept out of school to work at home, or if there is only enough money to educate one child – it goes to the boy. In some countries, girls are not permitted to receive an education.

WORKSHEET #72 (CONTINUED)

Fifteen-year-old Malala Yousafzai of Pakistan was marked for execution because she championed the right of girls to receive education in her homeland.

Gunmen shot her in the head while she was returning home from school on October 9, 2012. Remarkably, the bullet came within a few fractions of an inch from killing her. She was airlifted to a hospital in England where she underwent extensive surgeries and survived a life-threatening infection. After three months, she had recovered to the point where she no longer needed to be hospitalized. She will have to undergo future surgeries in which doctors will try to rebuild her skull. Meanwhile, she is living in England with her parents and her two brothers.

Though nominated for a Nobel Peace Prize, she is still marked for death if she returns to her native land. The family vows to return to Pakistan when Malala is fully recovered.

- *Why do you think such intense opposition to the education of females exists in some parts of the world?*

- *What is the purpose/what benefits are derived from extreme forms of gender inequality?*

- *Do you think that gender inequality will always exist?*

WORKSHEET #73

NAME _____

1. *Portrayal of Women in Advertisements*

   Description of a television advertisement for beer:

   Two womens' disagreement over what makes Miller Lite beer so great quickly becomes a sexy fight. They rip each other's clothes off as they wrestle in a swimming pool then a conveniently placed mud pit. The scene switches and we see that the fight was a fantasy dreamed up by two guys in a bar.

   What does this advertisement say about women?

   What does it say about men?

   Is the gender message in this advertisement consistent with your beliefs about gender?

2. *Gender Roles*

   Has anyone ever been told to "act like a man" or "act like a lady"? What do those expectations mean?

Act Like A Man	Act Like a Lady
1.	1.
2.	2.
3.	3.
4.	4.

PART IX: READING

The Concept of Dowry

Dowry: This is the practice where the bride's family gives money or goods or property to the groom and his family in exchange for his willingness to marry their daughter.

Chinese businessman Wu Duanbiao gave his daughter's husband a dowry worth $150 million. Wu, who is the chairman of a very successful ceramics corporation, gave his daughter and her new husband four boxes of gold jewelry, millions of dollars deposited into their bank account, donations to local charities in their names, shares in the ceramics firm, two cars, and a great deal of property. A spokesman for Wu's firm confirmed the dowry.

The groom, who the bride has known since kindergarten, only makes about $24,000 a year. Reports of the Wu dowry and photographs of the bounty were published by a newspaper in China on the day after the wedding. The reporter commented that marrying a daughter from this province in China is "better than robbing a bank."

The dowry practice isn't uncommon in China, especially in certain provinces. The tradition is believed to ensure that the bride will be treated well by her husband and in-laws. Just last month, two other billionaires gave their daughter and niece dowries totaling in the millions

Dowry is a tradition for some in Chinese culture. The popularity of the dowry payment among the very wealthy is in contrast to much less affluent Chinese. In less affluent areas, eligible women are in short supply due to Chinese laws about single births and the preference for male over female babies. Some single men in China may pay a fee to find a bride.

The closest comparison to the dowry tradition in the United States is the expectation that the bride's family will pay for the wedding. This tradition has changed. Today, the parents of the groom are sharing wedding expenses with the parents of the bride. In a growing number of cases, the couple takes on financial responsibility for the wedding.

NAME _____

The practice of dowries in some countries, such as India, is a serious problem that affects women from all levels of society.

Are you in favor of the concept of dowry? Why or why not?

How could dowries sometimes lead to serious problems – even deaths?

_____

_____

_____

_____

_____

_____

_____

_____

_____

_____

_____

_____

_____

_____

_____

_____

_____

_____

_____

_____

REFERENCES

Bloomberg. *Wage Gap for U.S. Women Endures Even as Jobs Increase.* Oct. 25, 2012. Web. 8 April 2013. <www.bloomberg.com/news/2012-10-25/wage-gap-for-u-s-women-endures-even-as-jobs-increase.html>

Center for American Progress. *How Working Women Are Reshaping America's Families in the Economy and What It Means for Policymakers.* March 2010. Web 7 April 2013. <http://www.americanprogress.org/wp-content/uploads/issues/2010/03/pdf/our_ working_ nation.pdf>

Diamond, M. (2005). Interview with Professor Milton Diamond: transexuality, intersexuality, and others. In L. May (Ed.) *Everything you wanted to know but couldn't think of the question.* Australia: East Street Publications, 72-94.

Discovery. *10 Examples of Gender Inequality Around the World.* 2013. 8 April 2013. <dsc.discovery.com/tv-shows/curiosity/topics/examples-gender-inequality-around-world. htm>

Eliot, L. (2009). *Pink Brain, Blue Brain: How Small Differences Grow into Troublesome Gaps – and What We Can Do About It.* Boston, MA: Houghton Mifflin Harcourt.

Forti, G., Corona, G., Vignozi, L., Krausz, C., and Maggi, M. (2010). Klinefelter's syndrome: a clinical & therapeutical update. *Sex Development,* 4(4-5), 249-258.

Green, R.R., and Young, R. (2001). Hand preference, sexual preference, and transsexualism. *Archives of Sexual Behavior,* 30(6), 565-574.

Halpern, D.F. and LaMay, M.L. (2000). The smarter sex: a critical review of sex differences in intelligence. *Educational Psychology Review,* 12(2), 229-246.

Hare, L., Bernard, P., Sanchez, F., Baird, P.N., Vilain, E., Kennedy, T., and Harley, V.R. (2009). Androgen receptor repeat length polymorphism associated with male-to-female transsexualism. *Biological Psychology,* 65(1), 93-96.

Hassett, J.M., Siebert, E.R., and Wallen, K. (2008). Sex differences in rhesus monkey toy preferences parallel those of children. *Hormones & Behavior,* 54(3), 359-364.

Human Rights Campaign. *Hate Crimes and Violence Against Lesbian, Gay, Bisexual and Transgender People*. May 2009. Web 13 February 2014. www.hrc.org/files/assets/resources/Hatecrimesandviolenceagainstlgbtpeople_2009.pdf

Kruijver, F., Zhou, J.-N., Pool, C.W., Hofman, M.A., Gooren, L.J.G., and Swaab, D.F. (2000). Male to female transsexuals have female neuron numbers in a limbic nucleus. *Journal of Clinical Endocrinology and Metabolism*, 85, 2034-2041.

Lachance-Brzela, M. and Bouchard, G. (2010). Why do women do the lion's share of housework? a decade of research. *Sex Roles*, 63 (1-12), 767.

Richardson, D.J. and Hammock, G.S. (2007). Social context of human aggression: are we paying too much attention to gender? *Aggression & Violent Behavior*, 12(4), 417-426.

Simpson, K. (2001).The role of testosterone in aggression. *McGill Journal of Medicine*, 6, 32-40.

PART X

SEXUAL ORIENTATION

WORKSHEET #74

Models of Sexual Orientation

Sexual orientation is a person's predisposition in terms of emotional attachment, physical attraction, or sexual behavior to one or both sexes.

How is someone's sexual orientation determined?

The most obvious way to categorize a person's sexual orientation is through sexual behavior. Many of us tend to think of sexual orientation in very distinct categories: people are either heterosexual or homosexual, except for the occasional bisexual.

How would we classify the 13-year-old girl who has never had a romantic partner, but finds herself sexually attracted to other girls? What about the married man who has a romantic, loving relationship with his wife, but fantasizes about having sex with other men whenever the two of them have intercourse?

What do researchers say?

For more than half a century, sex researchers have used a scale developed by Alfred Kinsey and his colleagues (1948). Kinsey believed that it was inadequate to rely on the categories heterosexual and homosexual to describe sexual orientation. He developed a seven point scale which depicts sexuality on a continuum with "0" representing exclusively heterosexual behavior, "3" represent behavior that is equally heterosexual and homosexual, and "6" representing exclusively homosexual behavior. Though the Kinsey continuum was the first scale to suggest that these people's sexual behavior cannot be simply reduced to heterosexual and homosexual, it has some problems as well.

1. The categories are:

Exclusively heterosexual	Predominantly heterosexual, incidental homosexual	Predominantly heterosexual, more than incidental homosexual	Equally heterosexual and homosexual	Predominantly homosexual, more than incidental homosexual	Predominantly homosexual, incidental heterosexual	Exclusively homosexual

These categories are somewhat vague and open to interpretation.

2. The scale considers only behaviors, with no consideration given to emotions or fantasies.
3. The scale fails to account for changes over time.

As a result of the problems with Kinsey's scale, the Klein Sexual Orientation Grid was developed. This scale accounts for one's sexual behavior in the past, present, and in their ideal future, i.e.

	Past	Present	Future
Sexual Behavior			

WORKSHEET #74 (CONTINUED)

Seven categories are considered: sexual attraction, sexual behavior, sexual fantasies, emotional preference, social preference, self-identification, and heterosexual/homosexual lifestyle. The subject's responses may range from 0 to 6 – "0" meaning other sex only, "3" meaning both sexes equally, and "6" meaning same-sex only.

While in college, Debbie "sexually experimented" with her roommate during her freshman year. She has since married a man and has two children. Is she bisexual?

Ben says that he learned that some animals exhibit homosexual behavior. Is Ben correct?

WORKSHEET #75

Theories of Sexual Orientation

There are literally hundreds of theories which seek to explain what determines a person's sexual orientation. Developmental theories focus on the child's upbringing and environment to explain the origins of homosexuality. For many years, the most influential developmental theories were psychoanalytic theories. Sigmund Freud was one of the first proponents of the idea that adult homosexuality occurred as a result of the "developmental arrest of childhood instincts which prevent the development of a more mature heterosexual." Though no research supported his belief, Freud hypothesized male homosexuality was due to an emotionally distant father and intense attachment to the mother while female homosexuality stems from anger around not having a penis coupled with a defensive rejection of her father and all men.

Another researcher, Sandor Rado, viewed homosexuality as a phobic avoidance of the other sex resulting from parental prohibition against childhood sexuality. His assertation that homosexuality was a mental illness was widely accepted.

In 1957, psychologist Evelyn Hooker challenged the prevailing views of homosexuality. After obtaining research support from the National Institute of Mental Health, she conducted psychological tests and used personal histories and psychological evaluations to show that homosexuals were as well adjusted as heterosexuals. She found no evidence that homosexuality was a mental/psychological disorder, but rather, within the normal range of human behaviors (although the American Psychiatric Association did not declassify homosexuality as a mental illness until 1973).

Biological theories assert that differences in sexual orientation may be due to genetic factors, prenatal hormone exposure, birth order, and brain anatomy and physiology.

Concordance rates for siblings, twins, and adoptees suggest that there is likely a genetic component to homosexuality. This does not mean that a "gay gene" has been discovered, but that genetic factors may underlie sexual orientation (Langstrom et al., 2010).

Research has found that in families with multiple brothers, later born brothers from the same mother are more likely to be gay (Bogaert & Skorska, 2011). It is thought that this is because the birth of multiple males in some women increases the effects of anti-male antibodies on the sexual differentiation in the brain of the developing fetus.

WORKSHEET #75 (CONTINUED)

Research has shown possible brain differences in gay and straight men (the vast majority of research has been done on males). Recent physiological research has looked at a variety of factors, including spatial abilities, handedness, and finger lengths (Schwartz et al., 2010). Just as human behavior is complex, it is most likely that biological, psychological, and social factors interact to determine an individual's sexual orientation.

Note: Concordance rate is the extent to which two people (usually siblings or twins) share similar characteristics, such as sexual orientation.

WORKSHEET #76

NAME _____

Toward Understanding . . .

1. What is the first word that comes to mind when you hear the word, homosexual?

   _____

   _____

2. Try to remember as far back as you can. What were the first messages that you received about homosexuality and from whom?

   _____

   _____

3. Initial awareness of sexual orientation generally occurs at about eight years of age. Some gay youth share this information with family and friends early in their lives. Others are afraid to "come out" (that is, acknowledge to oneself and others that he or she is gay, lesbian, or bisexual). What are some of the risks young people face by coming out as gay, lesbian, or bisexual?

   _____

   _____

   _____

4. Answer this question with the first thing that comes to your mind:
   If I learned that my child was homosexual, I would

   _____

   _____

   _____

   _____

WORKSHEET #77

Homosexual Relationships Versus Heterosexual Relationships: How Different or Alike Are They?

1. Is it true that in gay and lesbian relationships, one partner plays the "man's role" and one partner plays the "woman's role"?

   _____

   _____

   _____

2. Is it true that when same-sex couples argue, physical violence is used much more than with heterosexual couples?

   _____

   _____

   _____

3. Who are more committed to their relationships – same-sex couples or married heterosexual couples?

   _____

   _____

   _____

4. Who has more sex – gay and lesbian couples or heterosexual couples?

   _____

   _____

   _____

WORKSHEET #78

Gays and Lesbians as Parents

Many same-sex couples have children from previous heterosexual relationships; some used a surrogate mother or artificial insemination and some adopt. The exact number of children who are being raised by gay or lesbian parents is difficult to determine. Still, according to a 2012 report by the Williams Institute, an estimated 110,000 gay or lesbian couples are raising children in the United States. The highest proportion live in the South, followed closely by the Northeast and the Pacific states. The report, which drew data from several population-based surveys, indicates that adoption by gay and lesbian couples is clearly increasing. Among couples with children, the proportion of same-sex couples who have adopted children has nearly doubled from 10% to 19% between 2000 and 2009.

Some people believe that children who are raised by gay or lesbian parents are more likely to identify as gay or lesbian or to exhibit confusion about their gender identity. Research has not found this to be true – in fact, the overwhelming majority of children who are raised by gays and lesbians grew up identifying as heterosexual (consider that conversely, most gays and lesbians were raised by heterosexuals).

Some are concerned that children will suffer emotional and psychological trauma as a result of being raised by gay or lesbian parents. However, scientific evidence suggests that children who grew up with one or two gay and/or lesbian parents do as well emotionally/psychologically, cognitively, socially, and sexually as children who are raised by heterosexual parents (American Psychological Association, 2005; Gartrell & Bos, 2010; Farr et al., 2010).

A long-term study of children raised by lesbians found that the children were less likely to suffer physical or sexual abuse than their peers who were raised by heterosexuals. This is thought to be due to the absence of adult heterosexual men in the household (Gartrell, Bos & Goldberg, 2010). There are fewer studies of children raised by gay men. One study by Bergman, et al. (2010) found that gay fathers are more likely than heterosexual fathers to put their children before their career and to strengthen bonds with their extended families after becoming fathers.

Children raised by gay or lesbian parents must go through their own "coming out" process, in that they need to decide if and when to share information about their family with others. Unfortunately, there is still discrimination against gays and lesbians in the United States. This discrimination can have a negative impact on children (Gatrell et al. (2005) found that children raised by lesbians, who had experienced homophobic encounters, showed more psychological distress than those who did not have similar experiences.

WORKSHEET #79

Adoption by Gays and Lesbians

- Some states have made same-sex adoptions impossible by limiting adoption to couples who are legally married.
    Your Reaction:

- On January 6, 2013, Republican president hopeful, Rick Santorum, told an audience in New Hampshire that children are better off with a father in prison than they would be if they were raised in a home with lesbian parents and no father at all.
    Your Reaction:

- Currently, there are literally hundreds of thousands of children who are in foster care or awaiting adoption in the U.S. A 2011 report by the Donaldson Adoption Institute found that of adoptions by gay or lesbians, 10% of the children placed were older than six years of age (it is typically very difficult for older children to find adoptive homes) and about 25% were older than three. Sixty percent of gay and lesbian couples adopted across races, and more than 50% of the children adopted by gays and lesbians had special needs.
    Your Reaction:

WORKSHEET #80

Statistics on Same-Sex Marriage

As of this writing…

- 38 U.S. states have banned same-sex marriage (through legislation).

- 11 U.S. states and the District of Columbia allow same-sex marriage (however, the federal government does not recognize the marriages in most states). They are: Connecticut, Iowa, Maine, Maryland, Massachusetts, Minnesota, New Hampshire, New Jersey, New York, Vermont, and Washington.

- 6 U.S. states allow civil unions between same-sex couples, but not marriage (some states allow civil unions but would ban same-sex marriage). They are: Colorado, Delaware, Hawaii, Illinois, New Jersey, and Rhode Island.

- 12 is the number of countries, worldwide, where same-sex marriage is legal in the entire country. They are: Argentina, Belgium, Canada, Denmark, France, Iceland, the Netherlands, Norway, Portugal, South Africa, Spain, and Sweden.

- 3 is the number of countries where same-sex marriage is legal in some parts of the country. They are: Brazil, Mexico, and the U.S.

- 646,000 was the number of same-sex households in the U.S. in 2010 according to the U.S. Census Bureau.

The Netherlands made same-sex marriage legal in 2001. It was the first country in the world to do so.

Same-sex marriage became legal in Massachusetts in 2004. It was the first state in the U.S. to do so.

In 1996, Pres. Bill Clinton signed the Defense of Marriage Act (he has since urged the Supreme Court to overturn DOMA). DOMA asserts that federal law recognizes marriage only between a man and a woman. As a result, same-sex couples that are married or in a civil union are not granted any federal benefits.

In March of 2013, the U.S. Supreme Court heard two same-sex marriage cases, including a constitutional challenge to the Defense of Marriage Act in the case of U.S.A. versus Windsor.*

On June 26, 2013, the Supreme Court struck down the Defense of Marriage Act, meaning that married same-sex couples would be entitled to federal benefits and they ruled that "Proposition 8" (which disallowed same-sex marriage in California) was unconstitutional. Both rulings were major victories for gay Americans.

WORKSHEET #80 (CONTINUED)

*Edie Windsor and her late spouse, Thea Spyer, were together for almost 42 years. After being together for 40 years, they went to Canada and were married in 2007. Less than two years later, Spyer passed away – following a 30 year battle with multiple sclerosis. Her death left her partner, Edie, with the $363,000 federal estate tax bill that would not have been levied if her spouse had been a man.

The 83-year-old widow from New York City decided to fight back.

WORKSHEET #81

Pros and Cons

In the United States, people are divided on whether or not same-sex marriage should be legal. The percentage of Americans opposed to same-sex marriage has dropped considerably, from 68% in 1996 to 48% in 2012 according to a Gallup poll.

Opponents to the legislation of same-sex marriage often cite tradition or religious beliefs as the source of their opposition. Some opposition is based on the fact that gay or lesbian couples cannot procreate.

Supporters of same-sex marriage often do so from a human rights standpoint, asserting that the right to affirm one's love for a life partner is not dependent on sexual orientation.

1. *Some people respond to the 'tradition' argument against same-sex marriage (i.e. that we have no right to interfere with the institution of marriage as it has existed for so many years) by referring to the 1967 Supreme Court decision which struck down interracial marriage. What are your thoughts about the comparison?*

2. *You are having a conversation with two of your friends. One person is saying that they don't understand why gays and lesbians make a big deal about having the right to marry when they can have a civil union. Your other friend says that there is a big difference between marriage and civil union. They both look to you to resolve the dispute. How do marriage and civil union differ?*

WORKSHEET #82

NAME _____

Personal Inventory

This exercise describes a series of situations that you might come upon in your life. Read, each description and <u>immediately</u> write down your initial responses and feelings about the situation.

1. While walking in a parking garage you notice two men approaching a parked car. It seems that one is going to get in the car and the other is staying behind. As they say goodbye, the two men hug each other warmly and very briefly kiss on the mouth.

    _____

    _____

2. Your 19 year old cousin asks to talk with you privately, and you agree. Your young friend tells you that she/he is gay and says, "I would like to bring my partner to your house for your birthday celebration. Is that OK?"

    _____

    _____

3. You attend a meeting on campus for students in your major. You strike up a conversation with the student sitting next to you – seems like an interesting person to get to know. After a while the person asks, "Are you gay?"

    _____

    _____

4. Your child is 7 years old. The child unexpectedly asks you what a homosexual is.

    _____

    _____

WORKSHEET #82 (CONTINUED)

5. You are visiting your grandmother in a nursing home. Lucy, the woman sharing your grandmother's room, is quite ill. You notice an elderly woman sitting beside Lucy's bed holding her hand. You hear the woman say, "You are my darling. I have loved you for 50 years and I will always love you."

_____

_____

- *Did you feel uncomfortable at any point in this exercise? Can you identify any specific things that made you uncomfortable?*

- *Did you feel angry in response to any of the situations? Which ones? Can you identify the reasons for your anger?*

- *Were there any situations that seemed like "no big deal." Which ones?*

PART X: READING

Matthew Shepard's Story

Matthew Shepard was born on December 1st, 1976 in Casper, Wyoming. He went to public school in Casper until his junior year of high school when he moved with his family to Saudi Arabia. He finished high school abroad. In both schools he was elected by his peers to be a peer counselor. He was easy to talk to and made friends easily.

Matt had a great passion for equality. His experiences abroad fueled his love for travel and gave him the chance to make many new friends from around the world. Matt decided to attend college back in Wyoming, where he studied foreign relations and languages at the University of Wyoming in Laramie.

On October 7, 1998, Matthew was enjoying the evening at a Western type saloon in Wyoming that was popular with college students and others. A little after midnight, Matthew was ready to go home. Two men, Aaron McKinney and Russell Henderson, were about ready to leave too and offered to give him a ride home. Instead, they abducted Matt and drove him to a remote area east of Laramie, Wyoming. They tied Matthew to a fence. The two men severely beat him with the butt of a pistol. Seriously injured and barely conscious, Matthew was left to die in the cold of the night. His face was completely covered in blood. Almost 18 hours later, he was found by a bicyclist who initially mistook him for a scarecrow.

Matt died on October 12th at 12:53 AM at Poudre Valley Hospital with his family by his side. His memorial service was attended by friends and family from all over the world. The incident received immense media attention and inspired many to unite against bigotry and hate. In his life and death Matthew Shepard gave birth to a movement that more than a decade later would result in the passage of a federal law against bias crimes directed toward lesbian, gay, bisexual, or transgendered people.

Almost 15 years later, Mark Carson, a 32-year-old gay man was shot and killed early on a Saturday morning in Greenwich Village, New York City near the legendary Stonewall Inn, a popular establishment among the gay community where patrons famously clashed with police during a 1969 riot. According to police Commissioner Raymond W Kelly, the gunmen confronted Carson on the street and stalked him while shouting anti-gay slurs. The gunmen then pulled out a revolver and shot Carson point-blank in the face. Carson was taken to Beth Israel Medical Center, where he was pronounced dead on arrival. Elliot Morales, 33, was later arrested and charged with second-degree murder as a hate crime, along with menacing, and criminal possession of a weapon.

In a news conference after the shooting, Commissioner Kelly said New York City had seen a spike in bias related crimes in 2013 – a sharp deviation from an otherwise successful streak for the advancement of LGBT rights. This year alone has seen several states extend marriage rights to gay couples; a number of lawmakers – including two sitting Republican senators – have reversed their opposition to marriage equality; public figures (including a professional athlete) have come out as gay without provoking a backlash; and the Supreme Court issued two historic rulings that further validate same-sex marriage.

In New York City, perhaps the birthplace of the American gay rights movement, 22 bias related crimes had been reported in the first half of 2013, compared with just 13 during the same period last year. Carson was the fifth New York City victim of anti-gay violence in just the prior three weeks, though he was the first fatality.

LGBT advocates were quick to condemn the murder and highlight its significance for the civil rights battle ahead. "While our community has made progress, this is a stark and sobering reminder of the homophobia that still exists in our culture," said Wilson Cruz, GLAAD's national spokesperson, in a statement. "Until we rid ourselves of the discrimination that allows us to be seen as inferior and less than human, we will never truly be safe, even in one of the most exciting cities in the world."

The common term used to describe negative feelings toward gay people is homophobia. This is unfortunate since that is a medical term which implies that someone feels an uncontrollable intense fear. The more appropriate word is *heterosexism*. Heterosexism is the assumption that all people should be heterosexual and that heterosexuality is superior. It includes the stigmatization, denial, and/or denegration of anything non-heterosexual. The attitude is used to justify the mistreatment, discrimination, and harassment of gay, lesbian, bisexual, and transgender individuals.

NAME _____

1. *Considering the case of Matthew Shepard and other hate crimes – why do some people feel such anger toward people they often don't even know? In your opinion, where does that come from?*

2. *Do you think that someone who is heterosexist can change? Explain.*

_____

_____

_____

_____

_____

_____

_____

_____

_____

_____

_____

_____

_____

_____

_____

_____

_____

_____

_____

REFERENCES

American Psychological Association. *Lesbian and Gay Parenting Committee on Lesbian, Gay, & Bisexual Concerns.* 2005. Web. 27 April 2013. <www.apa.org/pi/lgbt/resources/parenting-full.pdf>

Bergman, K., Ritchie J., Rubio, R., Green, J., and Padron, E. (2010). Gay men who become fathers via surrogacy: the transition into parenthood. *Journal of GLBT Family Studies,* 6(2), 111-141.

Bogaert, A.F. and Skorska, M. (2011). Sexual orientation, fraternal birth order, and the maternal immune hypothesis: a review. *Frontiers in Neuroendocrinology,* 32(2), 247-254.

Evan B. Donaldson Adoption Institute. *Expanding Resources for Children III: Research-Based Practices in Adoption by Gays and Lesbians.* Oct. 2011. Web. 27 April 2013. <www.adoptioninstitute.org/publications/2011_10_Expanding_Resources_ BestPractices. pdf>

Farr, R.H., Forssell, S.L., and Patterson, C.J. (2010). Parenting and child development in adoptive families: does parental sexual orientation matter? *Applied Developmental Science,* 14(3), 164-178.

Gallup Politics. *Half of Americans Support Legal Gay Marriage.* May 8, 2012. Web. 27 April 2013. <www.gallup.com/poll/154529/half-americans-support-legal-gay-marriage.aspx>

Gartrell, N. and Bos, H. (2010). U.S. national longitudinal lesbian family study: psychological adjustment of 17-year-old adolescents. *Pediatrics,* 126(1), 1-9.

Gartrell N., Bos H., and Goldberg N. (2010). Adolescents of the U.S. national longitudinal lesbian family study: sexual orientation, sexual behavior, and sexual risk exposure. *Archives of Sexual Behavior,* doi:10.1007/s10508-010-9692-210.1007/s.

Gartrell, N., Rodas, C., Deck, A., Peyser, J., and Banks, A. (2005). Interviews with 10-year-old children. *American Journal of Orthopsychiatry,* 75(4). Web. 27 April 2013. <www.nllfs.org/images/uploads/pdf/NLLFS-4-interviews-with-10-year-olds-2005.pdf>

Hooker, E. (1957). The adjustment of the male overt homosexual. *Journal of Projective Techniques,* 21, 18-31.

Kinsey, A., Pomeroy, W.B., and Martin, C.E. (1948). *Sexual behavior in the human male.* Philadelphia: Saunders.

Langström, N., Rahman, Q., Carlstrom, E., and Lichtenstein. P. (2010). Genetic and environmental effects on same-sex sexual behavior: a population study of twins in Sweden *Archives of Sexual Behavior*, 39, 75-30.

Rado, S. (1949). An adaptational view of sexual behavior. In P.H. Hoch & J. Zubin (Eds.), *Psychosexual development in health and disease.* New York: Grune and Stratton. 159-189.

Schwartz, G., Kim, R., Kolundzisa, A., Rieger, G., and Saunders, A. (2010). Biodemographic and physical correlates of sexual orientation in men. *Archives of Sexual Behavior*, 39, 93-109.

Williams Institute. *Census & LGBT Demographic Studies.* March 2013. Web. 27 April 2013.

PART XI

SEXUAL
VICTIMIZATION

WORKSHEET #83

Rape and Sexual Assault

In the past, *rape* was defined as a man's non-consensual penal penetration into a woman's vagina. Today, the definition of rape has been expanded considerably to include non-consensual sexual penetration of a man or woman's body by physical force or the threat of harm. The unwanted penetration includes objects (not just the penis), and penetration includes the mouth and anus (not just the vagina). There is no one universal definition of rape. It not only may vary among countries, but from U.S. state to state as well.

Sexual assault is a more general term which encompasses any type of sexual contact that occurs without consent. Coercion can be psychological or physical and can include taking advantage of someone because of his or her intellectual deficiencies, impaired ability to give consent (as may occur with intoxication), or age.

It is difficult to assess the incidence of rapes and sexual assaults in the U.S. because of under-reporting. The Bureau of Justice Statistics (BJS) reports that between 1992 and 2000, the vast majority of rapes and sexual assaults perpetrated against women and girls in the United States were not reported to the police. Only 36 percent of rapes, 34 percent of attempted rapes, and 26 percent of sexual assaults, were reported (Rennison, 2002). Reasons for not reporting rape or sexual assault vary among individuals, but some of the most common reasons include:

- self-blame
- shame/desire to keep the assault a private matter
- fear of not being believed
- fear of reprisal from the attacker
- lack of trust in the criminal justice system
                  (DuMont et al., 2003; Wolitsky-Taylor et al., 2010)

WORKSHEET #84

Research on Sexual Violence

Research on sexual violence tells us....

- *Although both men and women can be raped, the vast majority of victims are female.* Though most rapes are never reported to the police, it is estimated that 1 of every 6 women (17.6%) and 1 of every 33 men (3%) have experienced an attempted or completed rape in their lifetime (Tjaden & Thoennes, 2006).

- *Most perpetrators of sexual assault are known to the victims.* Among victims ages 18 to 29, two-thirds had a prior relationship with the offender. The Bureau of Justice Statistics (BJS) reports that 6 in 10 rape or sexual assault victims said that they were assaulted by an intimate partner, relative, friend, or acquaintance. A study of sexual victimization of college women showed that 9 out of 10 victims knew the person who sexually victimized them (Fisher et al., 2000).

- *Women are significantly more likely than men to be injured during an assault.* A study by the U.S. Department of Justice found that 31.5 percent of female rape victims, compared with 16.1 percent of male rape victims, reported being injured during their most recent rape (Thoennes & Tjaden, 2000).

- *Sexual violence may begin early in life.* Researchers also found that among female rape victims surveyed, more than half (54%) were younger than 18; 32.4% were ages 12 - 17; and 21.6% were younger than age 12 at time of victimization (Thoenes & Tjaden, 2000). Seventy-one percent of male victims were first raped before their 18th birthday; 16.6% were 18 to 24 years old; and 12.3% were 25 or older (Tjaden & Thoennes, 2006).

- *Victims who were using drugs or alcohol before rape are much less likely to report the rape* (Wolitzky-Taylor et al., 2010).

WORKSHEET #85

Characteristics of Rapists

There is no one description of rapists. It is difficult to make generalizations about rapists, because most information that is gathered is about men who are *convicted* of rape. While most rapists are known by their victim, many rapes go unreported, and many men who were convicted of rape are strangers to their victims.

Still, research tells us that rapists are most often single males between the ages of 15 and 30. Most convicted rapists are serial offenders with an average of six victims. They often have histories of childhood physical abuse, dating violence, or intimate partner violence. They have a strong tendency toward aggressive behavior, exhibit high levels of rape myth acceptance, and acceptance of violence toward women (Lisak & Miller, 2002; Masser et al., 2006; Langevin et al., 2007; Cavanaugh et al., 2011; Chapleau & Oswald, 2010).

In a well-known study about the potential to rape, 356 college-age heterosexual men were asked, "If you could be assured that no one would know and that you in no way could be punished for forcing a woman to do something she really didn't want to do (sexually), how likely, if it all, would you be to commit such an act?" Sixty percent indicated that 'under the right circumstances' there was some likelihood that they would use force, rape, or both (Briere & Malamuth, 1983). Another study found that 58% of men admitted to committing a sex act on a woman who was unable to consent or who had made her lack of consent clear (Parkhill & Abbey, 2008).

WORKSHEET #86

Rape Myths

Rape myths are defined as prejudicial and stereotyped beliefs about rape, rape victims, and rapists. They lead to the attitude that rape is justified by rationalizing what occurred and who might be at fault (Burt, 1980).

The following are some of the more common rape myths:

- Women often lie/make false claims of rape.
- Women bring rape upon themselves by their appearance and behavior.
- Women could resist rape if they really wanted to.
- Men who rape do so because they cannot control their sexual desires.
- A man cannot rape his wife.
- Men cannot be raped.

A woman is more likely to be blamed for a rape if:

- She knows her assailant.
- No weapon was used.
- On a date, the woman allowed the man to pay.
- On a date, the woman went to the man's home.
- She had been at a bar.
- She is young and attractive.
    (Bassow & Minieri, 2011; Clarke & Lawson, 2009)

Who accepts rape myths?

- Males are generally more accepting of rape myths than women.
- Rape myths are more accepted by people who are more accepting of interpersonal violence and sex role stereotypes.
- Some victims of sexual assault accept rape myths. They are more likely to blame themselves for their attack, and have more difficulties with psychological adjustment.

WORKSHEET #87

Types of Rape

The type of relationship between the assailant and the victim is one way to define the type of rape. Examples include:

1. ***Stranger Rape***

    Fewer than one out of five rapes against women and one out of four rapes against men are committed by a stranger. Rapists who assault strangers are:

   - most likely to re-offend
   - most likely to be charged and convicted
   - generally receive more severe punishments than rapists who know their victims

   (Tjaden & Thoennes, 2006)

2. ***Date Rape***

   Date rape occurs when there is forced or coerced sex within a dating relationship. 'Drug facilitated rape' typically involves the use of a date rape drug, such as Rohypnol, GHB, ketamine, and Xanax. All of these drugs have properties that deal with memory impairment, loss of inhibitions, and/or sedation. The effects of Rohypnol – sedation, blackouts, and amnesia – typically last for 4 to 6 hours. Because it is tasteless and colorless, "roofies" may be slipped into the drink of an unsuspecting person.

   Alcohol is the number one drug used to facilitate a sexual assault. Of rapes that take place on college campuses, 74% of perpetrators and 55% of victims had been drinking alcohol at the time of the attack (Abbey, 2002).

   Of college women who are raped, only 25% describe it as rape and only 10% report the rape.

3. ***Marital Rape***

   Until 1993, it was legal in some states for a man to have sex with his wife against her wishes. Currently, 30 states have exemptions for husbands to force sex under certain conditions – if, for example, his wife is unconscious, sleeping, or mentally impaired (Bergen, 2006).

   It is estimated that between 8 and 14% of women are raped by their husbands or ex-husbands and the number is much higher in battered women (Ferro, Cermele, & Salzman, 2008). The attack usually occurs when the man has been drinking. Motives for marital rape include domination and degradation. Marital rape is the least likely type of rape to be reported. Women who remain with their husbands often endure repeated attacks.

4. *Rape of Men*

It is estimated that 3% of men in the U.S. have experienced a completed or attempted rape within their lifetime (Tjaden & Thoennes, 2006) though the number may actually be higher due to underreporting. Gay men have been found to be raped at a higher rate than heterosexual men.

Twenty-one percent of prisoners report being victims of forced sexual contact while in prison (Struckman-Johnson, 1994). Prison rape is often perpetrated by heterosexual men as an expression of power and dominance. Male prisoners are most likely to be sexually assaulted by other male prisoners, while female prisoners are most often raped by prison employees.

5. *Statutory Rape*

Statutory rape is sexual intercourse that occurs between an adult and someone who is not a child but who is below the age of consent. In statutory rape, the sex need not be forced.

- *Age of consent.* This is the age at which an individual can legally consent to sexual intercourse under any circumstances.

- *Minimum age of victim.* This is the age below which an individual cannot consent to sexual intercourse under any circumstances.

- *Age differential.* If the victim is above the minimum age and below the age of consent, the age differential is the maximum difference in age between the victim and the defendant where an individual can legally consent to sexual intercourse.

- *Minimum age of defendant in order to prosecute.* This is the age below which an individual cannot be prosecuted for engaging in sexual activities with minors.

Specific statuary rape laws vary from state to state. For example:

In New Jersey the age of consent is 16, but individuals who are at least 13 years of age can legally engage in sexual activities if the defendant is less than four years older than the victim.

- In the District of Columbia it is illegal to engage in sexual intercourse with someone who was under the age of consent (16) if the defendant is four more years older than the victim.

- In Ohio, sexual intercourse with someone under 13 years of age is illegal regardless of the age of the defendant. However, if the victim is above the   minimum age requirement (13) and below the age of consent (16), it is only illegal to engage in sexual intercourse with that individual if the defendant is at least 18 years of age (U.S. Dept. of Health & Human Services, 2012).

WORKSHEET #88

Two Cases

First Case

One evening back in 1983, 21-year-old Cheryl Araujo put her two daughters to sleep in her apartment in New Bedford, Massachusetts following her older daughter's third birthday party. She then left her children with her boyfriend (and father of her children) to buy cigarettes at a nearby store at 9 PM.

Two local stores were closed, so she walked a block to Big Dan's Tavern. She bought the cigarettes and then had a drink with a woman at a table. They chatted and flirted with two men who were shooting pool. The other woman left. Cheryl put her glass on the bar and walked toward the door to leave. Suddenly, a man in back of her grabbed the collar of her jacket and another grabbed her feet. They dragged her across the floor to the pool table and stripped off her jeans.

"I could hear people laughing, cheering and yelling from near the bar," the woman recalled in court. "My head was hanging off the edge of the pool table.... I was begging for help. I was pleading. I was screaming.... The man that was holding me down had grabbed me by the hair. The more I screamed, the tighter he pulled."

Then, reportedly, began a terrifying, 90 minute gang rape attack by six men. The woman could hear men laughing and shouting, "Do it! Do it!" Prosecutors later said they "cheered like it was a baseball game," and a detective described the accused rapists as acting "like a pack of sharks on a feeding frenzy." The bartender and three other men witnessed the rape, but two maintained that they were threatened and afraid to call police.

After one alleged rapist stepped away to talk with his friends, Araujo escaped – fleeing into the street at about 12:30 AM wearing only an unzipped jacket and a sock. She flagged down three men in a passing pickup truck, who heard her screaming that she had been raped. Cut and bruised, the woman was so traumatized she threw her arms around the neck of a passenger Daniel O'Neil. "I wouldn't let go for at least five minutes," she later said.

After the incident four original defendants were released on only $1000 bail. Two others were later indicted as accessories for pinning the alleged victim down on the pool table.

During the trial, the defendant's attorneys brutally cross-examined Araujo. She was painted as an "unwed mother" (a scandal in those days) who left her children at home with her boyfriend to buy cigarettes, not milk or bread for her children. Many people in the small town asked what kind of mother leaves her children to buy cigarettes.

Furthermore, she was dressed in tight jeans and a jacket and went into a bar alone. Many of the locals assumed she was a prostitute. What kind of woman goes out of her house at night to a bar? For many in the town, the answer was clear – she was 'asking for it.'

The case was tried in a neighboring town. Six men were originally charged with the rape. Four of the defendants were convicted of aggravated rape and two men were acquitted of the charges.

Second Case

In August 2012, two high school football players were convicted in an Ohio rape case that focused on social media. In a trial that divided the football crazed town of Steubenville, two young men (one 16 and one 17 years of age) were found guilty of raping a drunk 16-year-old girl.

The Judge announced his decision after reviewing evidence presented over four days of testimony in the case against the teens, who were tried as juveniles. One of the defendants was also found guilty of disseminating a nude photo of a minor. The ruling brings an end to a trial that gained media attention for its lurid text messages, cell phone pictures and videos, and social media posts surrounding the sexual abuse of the girl.

The victim was not in the courtroom when the ruling was read, but her mother gave a statement after the judge's ruling. "Human compassion is not taught by a teacher, a coach or a parent. It is a God-given gift instilled in all of us," the victim's mother said after court was adjourned. "They displayed not only a lack of this compassion, but a lack of any moral code," the woman said of the young men. She said that her daughter will persevere and move on, adding that she has pity for the teens.

The 17-year-old was sentenced to a minimum of two years in a juvenile correctional facility. The 16-year-old was sentenced to a minimum of one year, but both could be in detention until the age of 21. The two will be required to register as sex offenders and undergo treatment while in detention. The judge said he would postpone the hearing about which sexual offender category in which they will be registered until the end of their incarceration.

The two teen boys were accused of raping the girl during a series of end of summer parties in August 2012. According to prosecutors, each of them penetrated the victim's vagina with his fingers, an act that constitutes rape under Ohio law if it is not consensual. Attorneys for the two boys had said they were not guilty.

WORKSHEET #88 (CONTINUED)

At the heart of the case was the question of whether the victim was too drunk on the night of August 11 and the early morning of August 12 to understand what was happening to her and to consent. The trial focused on text messages.

The victim testified that she remembered little about the night because she was drunk. During closing statements, attorneys for the two teens argued that the state failed to prove beyond a reasonable doubt that their clients raped the girl. Prosecutors told the judge there is no question the girl was "substantially impaired."

The victim says she remembers little of the night in question. The girl testified that she remembered drinking at the first big party of the night. The next thing she remembered, she told the court, was waking up in the morning naked on a couch in an unfamiliar house. She covered herself with a blanket while she looked for her clothes. She testified that she could not find her underwear, earrings or cell phone. She testified that she was "too embarrassed to ask what happened that night because I didn't remember." The girl told the court she had a flashback memory of throwing up in the street somewhere sometime after she left the first party.

The community was severely divided. Critics have accused community leaders of trying to cover up misconduct by the teens who were players on the powerhouse "Big Red" football team. Attorneys for the two young men challenged the credibility of the victim, calling two of the 16-year-old's former friends to testify. One witness, a 17-year-old, testified that the victim told her she believed she had been drugged the night of the assault, an allegation the witness said she did not believe because the girl "lies about things." The defense attempted to question the two teens about the victim's sexual history, but the judge did not allow most of the line of questioning. Ohio, like most states, has a rape shield law that limits the amount of information about the alleged victim's sexual history that can be explored in court.

On Friday, three teens, all self-described friends of the co-defendants, testified that they saw the teens engage in sexual contact with the girl. One of the witnesses – identified as a 17-year-old Steubenville football player and wrestler – testified that he used his cell phone to record one of the teens putting his fingers inside the girl's vagina during a drive from one party to another. He said he deleted the video the next morning, when he realized it was wrong. The teen also testified that the 17-year-old later attempted to have the girl perform an oral sex act on him in the basement of a home. "She didn't really respond to it," he said.

WORKSHEET #88 (CONTINUED)

NAME _____

First Case

The case received national attention. Many hoped that it would set a precedent for criminalizing the behavior of cheering onlookers. Instead, it became a standard for 'blaming the victim' – a strategy that has been employed by many a defense attorney.

Do you think that Cheryl Araujo is more to blame than a woman who was raped in her home by an intruder who was a stranger to the victim? Explain.

_____

_____

_____

_____

_____

Second Case

Many people felt that the teens needed to be held responsible for behavior in which they toyed with, humiliated, and sexually assaulted a 16-year-old girl who was not in any position to defend herself. They applauded their conviction and incarceration. Others felt that nothing would be served by 'ruining the lives' of two teenage boys who made very poor judgments when dealing with a very drunk girl.

What do you think?

_____

_____

_____

_____

_____

WORKSHEET #89

Prison Time for Rapists?

Based on statistics from the FBI, the Justice Department and the National Center for Policy Analysis, The Rape, Abuse and Incest National Network (RAINN) has compiled the following breakdown:

OUT OF EVERY 100 RAPES

46 get reported to the police

12 lead to an arrest

9 get prosecuted

5 lead to a felony conviction

3 rapists will spend even a single day in prison

THE OTHER 97 WILL WALK FREE

Factoring in unreported rapes, only about three percent of rapists will ever serve a day in prison. Even when the crime is reported, it is not likely to lead to an arrest and prosecution (RAINN, 2013).

Why do you think that the arrest and prosecution rate of reported rapes is so low?

_____

_____

_____

_____

_____

_____

_____

_____

WORKSHEET #90

Intimate Partner Violence

Intimate partner violence (IPV) is a pattern of abusive behaviors designed to exert power and control over a person in an intimate relationship such as marriage, cohabitation, or dating.

It may involve physical abuse (for example: hitting, shoving, threats of physical harm), psychological abuse (for example: behavior intended to humiliate, intimidate, or isolate one's partner), or economic abuse (for example: denying funds or access to health care). Physical abuse is typically accompanied by psychological abuse, and in a significant number of cases, sexual abuse as well.

There was a time when husbands could legally beat their wives. Domestic violence or intimate partner violence was ignored, if not accepted, both here and elsewhere. A 1954 report from Scotland Yard read, "There are only about 20 murders a year in London and not all are serious – some are just husbands killing their wives." IPV can happen to males or females of any age and it is found among all racial, ethnic, and socioeconomic classes. IPV can occur in heterosexual or same-sex relationships. However, in same-sex relationships, there is less social support, less availability of psychological services, and fear of being "outed" when seeking help.

WORKSHEET #91

Consequences of IPV

According to the Centers for Disease Control more than 12 million men and women are victims of IPV each year.

On average, between 2001 and 2005, nonfatal intimate partner victimizations represented:

- 22% of nonfatal violent victimizations against females age 12 and older
- 4% of nonfatal violent victimizations against males age 12 and older

While male victims are more likely than female victims to be grabbed, held, or tripped (Bureau of Justice Statistics, 2007), female victims of IPV are at greater risk than male victims for sustaining physical and psychological injury (Cercone, Beach & Arias, 2005).

On average, between 2001 and 2005, more than one third of male victims of nonfatal intimate partner violence were injured. While 4% were seriously injured, 36% suffered minor injuries (Bureau of Justice Statistics, 2007). Thirty-three percent of all women's injuries coming into an emergency room are a result of attack by a husband, boyfriend, ex-boyfriend, parent, or child. One in four pregnant women is a victim of IPV. (Carlson, et al., 2004; Silent Witness National Initiative, 2013). Regardless of who initiates the violence, women are 7 to 10 times more likely than men to be injured in acts of intimate partner violence (Bureau of Justice Statistics, 2007).

According to the Bureau of Justice Statistics (Silent Witness National Initiative, 2013), in 2004:

- About one third of female murder victims were killed by an intimate (on average, more than three women are murdered by their husbands or boyfriends each day).
- About 3% of male murder victims were killed by an intimate.
- Of all female murder victims, the proportion killed by an intimate declined slightly until 1995 when the proportion began increasing, although it has stabilized recently.
- Of male murder victims, the proportion killed by an intimate has dropped by about one third between 1976 and 2004.

WORKSHEET #92

Psychological Effects of IPV

Individuals who have been victimized by an intimate partner – recently or in the past – may experience one or many of the following:

- depression
- suicidal thoughts and/or behavior
- anxiety
- low self-esteem
- inability to trust
- fear of intimacy
- isolation
- risky behaviors (unhealthy eating, risky sexual behaviors, and substance abuse)
- posttraumatic stress disorder
- emotional detachment
- sleep disturbances
- flashbacks
- poor physical health (frequent headaches, chronic pain, and activity limitations)
             (American Psychological Association, 2013)

The American psychological Association recommends the following:

What can you do to help yourself?

- Connect with supportive and caring people, not those who might blame you for the abuse.

- Secure a restraining or protective order if necessary – it prohibits an individual from harassing, threatening, approaching, accosting, or even contacting you. Always keep it with you.

- Seek help from a psychologist or other licensed mental health provider, contact your doctor or other primary health care provider, and take advantage of services at centers or shelters for battered women.

WORKSHEET #92 (CONTINUED)

Safety planning

- Identify your partner's use and level of force so that you can tell when you and your children are in danger before it occurs.

- Identify safe areas of the house where there are no weapons (e.g. not the kitchen) and there are ways to escape. If arguments begin, try to move to one of those areas.

- If possible, have a phone handy at all times and know what numbers to call for help.

- Don't be afraid to call the police.

- Let trusted friends and neighbors know of your situation, and develop a plan and visual signal for when you need help.

- Pack a bag (including money, an extra set of keys, copies of important documents, extra clothes and medicines) and leave it in a safe place.

- Teach your children how to get help. Instruct them not to get involved in the violence between you and your partner. Plan a code word to signal when to get help or leave the house.

- Practice how to get out safely. Practice with your children.

- Call a domestic violence hotline periodically to assess your options and get support and understanding.

Why Do Some People Stay in Abusive Relationships?

Generally, abusive relationships involve a pattern of abuse rather than an isolated incident. Many women, in particular, find excuses for their partner's behavior and accept their apology, believing that the abuse will not happen again.

The Harvard Guide to Women's Health (Carlson et al., 2004) suggests a number of factors that may contribute to a woman's decision to remain with an abusive partner:

- The impulse to forgive reflects a woman's low self-esteem or discomfort expressing anger or aggression

- Adherence to traditional gender roles

- Religious or cultural pressures

- Ties to her partner through children or finances

- The feeling that it is her duty to help her troubled partner

- Fear that her partner will find her and hurt her or their children

WORKSHEET #93

Defining Child Sexual Abuse

Child sexual abuse (CSA) is defined as sexual behavior that occurs between an adult and a minor. The sexual behavior can include, but is not limited to inappropriate touching, genital fondling, masturbation, digital penetration, oral sex, vaginal intercourse, anal intercourse, and sending electronic sexual images to children.

When discussing the sexual abuse of minors, the scientific literature also includes the term – *pedophilia*. Pedophilia is defined as an adult's compulsive desire to engage in sexual behavior with a child or children who are prepubescent (13 years of age or younger). Pedophilia is classified as a mental disorder. To be considered pedophilia, these fantasies, urges, or behaviors (all of which bring about sexual arousal) need to have existed for a period of six months or longer.

Another term that is sometimes used in the context of CSA is *incest*. Incest is defined as sexual contact between people who are related or who are in a care-giving relationship such as stepparent and stepchild. Father-daughter is the most reported form of incest, followed by uncle-niece, stepfather-stepdaughter, and brother-sister.

WORKSHEET #94

Child Sexual Abuse in the U.S. – Statistics

Who Are the Victims?

- 1 in 3 girls and 1 in 6 boys are sexually abused before the age of 18.
- 1 in 5 youths received a sexual approach or solicitation over the Internet in the past year.
- The average age for first abuse is 9.9 years for boys and 9.6 years for girls.
- Abuse typically occurs within a long-term, on-going relationship between the offender and victim, escalates over time and lasts an average of four years.
- More than 90% of sexual abusers of children are male. Of those men, more than three fourths are heterosexual.
- Many begin sexually abusing children while in their teens.
- Less than 10% of child sexual abuse is reported to the police.
- Children are most vulnerable between ages 8 and 12.
- 29% of forcible rapes occurred when the victim was under 11 years old.
- 15% of sexual assault and rape victims are under the age of 12.
- 44% of sexual assault and rape victims are under age 18.
- Children with disabilities are 4 to 5 times more vulnerable to sexual abuse than their non-disabled peers.
- Nearly 30% of child sexual assault victims identified by child protective service agencies were between 4 and 7 years of age.
- 93% of juvenile sexual assault victims knew their attackers, 34.2% of attackers were family members, 58.7% were acquaintances and only 7% of the perpetrators were strangers to the victim.
- Nearly 50% of all the victims of forcible sodomy or sexual assault with an object are children under the age of 12.
- 60% of girls who had sex before the age of 15 were coerced by males averaging 6 years their senior.
- Women who experienced sexual abuse as a child are 2 to 3 times more likely to be sexually assaulted later in life.
- Like rape, child molestation is one of the most underreported crimes: only 1-10% are ever disclosed.
- Fabricated sexual abuse reports constitute only 1% to 4% of all reported cases. Of these reports, 75% are reported by adults. Children fabricate sexual abuse less than 1% of the time.
- IT IS ESTIMATED THAT THERE ARE 60 MILLION SURVIVORS OF CHILDHOOD SEXUAL ABUSE IN AMERICA TODAY.

WORKSHEET #94 (CONTINUED)

What Are the Effects of Child Sexual Abuse?

- The experience of sexual abuse for a child distorts her or his self-concept and ability to form healthy relationships as adults.

- High rates of depression, anxiety, substance abuse, interpersonal dysfunction, sexual problems, and suicidal tendencies have all been identified to varying degrees among men and women who survive child sexual abuse.

- Adolescents with a history of sexual abuse are significantly more likely to engage in sexual behavior that puts them at risk for HIV infection.

- A 1996 report from the U.S. Department of Justice estimated rape and sexual abuse of children to cost $1.5 billion in medical expenses annually to U.S. victims

- When sexually abused children are not treated, society must later deal with resulting problems such as mental health issues, drug and alcohol abuse, crime, suicide, and the perpetuation of a cycle of sexual abuse.

> (Arata, 2002; Snyder, 2000; Finkelhor, 2009; Finkelhor, Ormrod, & Chaffin, 2009, DeMarni & Goldsmith, 2010; and Parents for Megan's Law, 2007)

Treatment

There is no single treatment for sex offenders. All are designed to alter the behavior of the child molester. Some choose to attend support groups as well as individual psychotherapy. Some receive medications designed to reduce the sexual urges.

Society attempts to prevent repeated child sexual abuse by identifying convicted molesters and informing the public of their whereabouts. *'Megan's Law'* refers to laws in the U.S. requiring registration and public notification about sex offenders. *The law requires each state to have a procedure for notifying the public about convicted sex offenders who live in the community.* Within 30 days of release from incarceration, the sex offender must register with the state. The information is then made available to the community. The means by which the public is notified (i.e. flyers, Internet) differs from state to state.

The *Adam Walsh Child Protection and Safety Act of 2006* eliminated the statute of limitations for prosecution of felony sex offenders involving minors. Victims may also sue their assailant in civil court in order to be financially compensated for their suffering.

WORKSHEET #95

*NAME*_____

Continuum of Harm

Each of the situations below may or may not dehumanize women and contribute to a rape supportive culture.

Rate the 9 behaviors or beliefs as: (A) extremely harmful (C) slightly harmful
(B)moderately harmful or (D) not harmful at all

Honking or whistling at s woman/girl walking down the street	
Telling a man or boy that he throws like a girl	
Yelling at your girlfriend for talking to another guy	
Refusing to wear a condom	
Believing that a woman's place is in the home with the kids	
Joking about how a serious girl 'needs to get laid'	
Looking at porn depicting women being physically and verbally abused	
Date rape	
Stranger rape	

WORKSHEET #95 (CONTINUED)

Explain the reason for your choices.

_____

_____

_____

_____

_____

_____

_____

_____

_____

_____

_____

_____

PART XI: READING

Bryant and the Rape Shield Law

On June 30, 2003, NBA superstar Kobe Bryant was indicted on charges of sexually assaulting a 19-year-old hotel desk clerk. On September 1, 2004, Colorado prosecutors decided to drop the case against Bryant after prosecutors said that the woman who alleged she had been assaulted would not agree to testify on the stand against the basketball superstar.

Bryant had checked into the Lodge and Spa at Cordillera in Colorado in June of 2003 in advance of having a surgical procedure performed at a nearby hospital. The woman accused Bryant of raping her in her hotel room the night before the surgery.

Records and transcripts of interviews between investigators and Bryant and his accuser as well as pretrial testimony have been widely circulated. The then 19-year-old woman who was a front desk employee had given Bryant a tour of the resort. She said that she and Bryant kissed for several minutes in his room before he became aggressive and began groping her. The woman also said she wanted him to kiss her and she said that she thought that he was "going to try and make a move on me" – but she did not wish to perform the sex acts which were forced upon her.

During his interview with detectives, Bryant said the woman told him she had hoped he would have sex with her, according to the transcript released Friday. He said the woman never cried and he repeatedly told detectives the sex was consensual. He also said she gave him a kiss goodbye before she left his room.

Several times during the questioning, Bryant asked detectives whether the woman wanted money from him.

Testimony from a detective, described what Bryant's accuser told him about the encounter: "He forced her to turn around, bent her over a chair, pulled her panties down and entered her from the rear." Asked the length of the encounter, the detective said, "Five minutes." The accuser also told the detective she was crying and said 'No' several times. The detective said that when he asked her how she knew that Bryant heard her she said that every time she said 'No' he tightened his hold around her.

A bellman and high school friend of the woman said she appeared to be very upset a short time after leaving Bryant's room. "As we started to walk to the time clock (she) grabbed my arm and started to cry and said that Kobe Bryant choked her," the bellman said in a police statement. "After we clocked out, I asked her to tell me everything, and that is when she told me that Kobe Bryant had forced sex with her."

He added: "She was very shaken and she was crying" as the two walked to their cars from the hotel.

The bellman said he followed her home, a drive of about 20 minutes, told her to tell her parents what happened and left. He said he called the next morning and learned that she had not yet told her parents.

The woman had called her former boyfriend, Matt Herr, who wrote in a statement that she was "very upset, claiming that Kobe Bryant had raped her."

Bryant was interviewed by a sheriff's investigator, Dan Loya. During the interview, Bryant initially denied having sex with the woman, then changed his account, saying that she initiated it after the investigators told him they had physical evidence indicating the two had sex.

Bryant asserted that the sex was totally consensual. When asked what made him believe that it was consensual, Bryant said, "Cause she started kissing me, (inaudible) then she bent over and (inaudible)," Bryant said.

Bryant said the woman offered to show him a tattoo of musical instruments and notes on her back, and she lowered her strap on her dress so he could see it. After that, he said, she kissed him and he kissed back. They caressed each other and she performed oral sex. Bryant said he held her by the neck from behind, she lifted her dress bent over a chair and they had sex. He said he stopped after she refused to let him do something he requested.

The woman told detectives that he held her by the neck hard enough to leave a small bruise on her jaw, bent her over a chair and pulled down her underwear. When the detective told Bryant the woman had experienced some bleeding, he said he was surprised because he hadn't noticed any blood.

Bryant also admitted to frequent similar encounters with another woman named "Michelle," who could testify that he also held her from behind. Bryant, who had been married for two years and had a five month old daughter, said his wife did not know about the other woman. He told investigators he was concerned about damage to his marriage, his career and his image if word of the rape allegation got out.

"Is there any way I can settle this, whatever it is?" Bryant asked. "Well, what do you mean by settle?" The detective replied. "If my wife found out that anybody made any type of allegations against me she would be infuriated," Bryant said.

Quickly, Bryant's lawyers showed how aggressive the defense would be. At the earliest opportunity Pamela Mackey, Bryant's attorney, attacked the accuser. Referring to photographs of the young woman's injury, Mackey asked in a preliminary hearing if it was "consistent with a person who had sex with three different men in three days." That suggestion, which Mackey could not or was unwilling to back up, pushed a promiscuous (and irrelevant) image of the accuser into the media.

Like most states, Colorado has a "rape shield law." The law attempts to protect victims from disclosures about their sexual conduct or reputation before or after an alleged assault. Still, in a controversial decision, the judge ruled that Bryant's attorneys could introduce evidence about the accuser's other sexual experiences.

Although the accuser never came forward publicly, she was subjected to an enormous amount of negative publicity. Despite the judge's order prohibiting the reporting of the accuser's name, her name, yearbook photo, phone number, home address, and e-mail address were reported. Websites created consumer products such as underwear and tank tops bearing the accuser's name and printed with derogatory statements such as "lying bitch." Some included digitally altered photographs depicting her in sexual positions with Bryant.

At grocery stores nationwide, tabloids labeled her as a "party girl" and implied that "women who party can't be rape victims." Even the mainstream press disclosed her age, hometown, college, and hobbies. It published details of her life including an alleged drug overdose, a break up with her boyfriend, and stories about her 'sexual history' that her alleged 'friends' shared on morning television and with newspapers and magazines.

There were hundreds of threats against the accuser's life, several of which led to arrests. Rumors surfaced in late November 2003 that intense media attack spurred the accuser to seek medical treatment, leave school, and move from her hometown after facing "public scorn, hatred, and ridicule." After receiving hundreds of e-mails daily – some containing death threats, others from men asking for dates – the accuser shut down her e-mail and phone accounts. In effect, her life was ruined over the course of the proceedings.

The dismissal ended a case that had generated intense emotions. Victim advocates condemned the decision of the judge to allow evidence of the accuser's sexual activity in the days surrounding her encounter with Bryant and efforts by his attorneys to attack her reputation.

The woman has filed a civil lawsuit against Bryant. His defenders have said she is now attempting to make money off the basketball player.

NAME _____

1. *Are there any situations in which the victim is more responsible for the rape than the rapist?*

2. *If the accused rapist is a popular figure (i.e. nationally known superstar or popular campus figure) are we less likely to believe the accuser? More likely? Why?*

_____

_____

_____

_____

_____

_____

_____

_____

_____

_____

_____

_____

_____

_____

_____

_____

_____

REFERENCES

Abbey, A. (2002). Alcohol-related sexual assault: a common problem among college students. *Journal of Studies on Alcohol and Drugs*, 14, 118-128.

American Psychological Association. *Intimate Partner Violence: Facts & Resources*. 2013. *APA*. Web. 21 May 2013. <www.apa.org/topics/violence/partner.aspx>

Arata, C. (2002). Child sexual abuse and sexual revictimization. *Clinical Psychology*, 9, 135-164.

Bassow, S.A. and Minieri, A. (2011). "You owe me": who pays, participant gender, and rape myth beliefs on perceptions of rape. *Journal of Interpersonal Violence*, 26(3), 479-497.

Bergen, R. (2006). Marital rape: research and directions. *National Sexual Violence Resource Center*. Web. 24 May 2013. <http://new.vawnet.org/Assoc_Files_VAWnet/AR_MaritalRapeRevised.pdg.>

Black, M.C., Basile, K.C., Breiding, M.J., Smith, S.G., Walters, M.L., Merrick, M.T., Chen, J., and Stevens, M.R. *The National Intimate Partner and Sexual Violence Survey (NISVS): 2010 Summary Report*. Atlanta, GA: National Center for Injury Prevention and Control, Centers for Disease Control and Prevention; 2011.

Briere, J. and Malamuth, N. (1983). Self-reported likelihood of sexually aggressive behavior: attitudinal versus sexual explanations. *Journal of Research in Personality*, 17, 315-323.

Bureau of Justice Statistics. *Intimate Partner Violence in the U.S.* 2007. *BJS*. Web. 14 May 2013.<www.bjs.gov/content/intimate/injury.cfm>

Burt, M. (1980). Cultural myths and support for rape. *Journal of Personality and Social Psychology*, 38, 217-230.

Carlson, K. J., Eisenstat, S. A., and Ziporyn, T. Z. (2004). *The new Harvard guide to women's health*. Cambridge, MA: Harvard University Press, 209.

Cavanaugh, C., Messing, J., Petras, H., Fowler, B., LaFlair, L., Kub, J., Agnew, J., Fitzgerald, S., Bolyard, R., and Campbell, J. (2011). Patterns of violence against women: a latent class analysis. Psychological trauma: theory, research, practice, and policy. *American Psychological Association*, doi:10.1037/a0023314

Cercone, J., Beach, S., and Arias, I. (2005). Gender symmetry in dating intimate partner violence: does similar behavior imply similar constructs? *Violence & Victims*, 20 (2), 207-208.

Chapleau, K.M. and Oswald, D.L. (2010). Power, sex, and rape myth acceptance: testing two models of rape proclivity. *Journal of Sex Research*, 47(1), 66-78.

Clarke, A.K. and Lawson, K.L. (2009). Women's judgments of sexual assault scenario: the role of prejudicial attitudes and victim weight. *Violence and Victims*, 24(2), 248-254.

DeMarni Cromer, L. and Goldsmith, R.E. (2010). Child sexual abuse myths: attitudes, beliefs and individual differences. *Journal of Child Sexual Abuse*, 19, 618-647.

Du Mont, J., Miller, K.L., and Myhr, T.L. (April 2003). "The role of 'real rape' and 'real victim' stereotypes in the police reporting practices of sexually assaulted women." *Violence Against Women*, 9(4), 466-486.

Ferro, C., Cermele, J., and Saltzman, A. (2008). Current perceptions of marital rape. *Journal of Interpersonal Violence*, 23, 764.

Finkelhor, D. (2009). The prevention of child sexual abuse. *Future of Children*, 19, 169-194.

Finkelhor, D., Ormrod, R., and Chaffin, M. (December, 2009). *Juveniles who commit sex offenses against minors*. Office of Juvenile Justice and Delinquency Prevention Bulletin.

Fisher, B.S., Cullen, F.T., and Turner, M.G. (2000). *The sexual victimization of college women*. Washington, DC: U.S. Department of Justice, Bureau of Justice Statistics and National Institute of Justice, NCJ 132369.

Langevin, R., Langevin, M., and Curnoe, S. (2007). Family size, birth order, and parental age among male paraphilics and sex offenders. *Archives of Sexual Behavior*, 36, 599-609.

Lisak. D. and Miller, P. (2002). Repeat rape and multiple offending among undetected rapists. *Violence and Victims*, 17(1), 73-84.

Masser, B., Viki, T., and Power, C. (2006). Hostile sexism and rape proclivity amongst men. *Sex Roles*, 54, 565-574.

Parents for Megan's Law and the Crime Victims Center (2007). *Statistics – Child Sexual Abuse.* Web. 20 May 2013. <http://www.parentsformeganslaw.org/public/statistics childSexualAbuse.html>

Parkhill, M. and Abbey, A. (2008). Does alcohol contribute to the confluence model of sexual assault perpetration? *Journal of Social and Clinical Psychology*, 27, 529-554.

Rape, Abuse and Incest National Network. *Reporting Rates.* 2013. *RAINN.* Web. 24 May 2013. <http://www.RAINN. org/get-information/statistics/reporting-rates>

Rennison, C.M. (August, 2002). *Rape and sexual assault: reporting to police and medical attention, 1992-2000.* Washington, DC: U.S. Department of Justice, Bureau of Justice Statistics, NCJ 194530.

Silent Witness National Initiative. (2013). *Statistics on Domestic Violence from US Dept. of Justice - Office of Justice Programs.* 2004. Web. 23 May 2013. <www.silentwitness.net/sub/violences.htm>

Snyder, H.N. (2000). *Sexual assault of young children as reported to law enforcement - victim incident, and offender characteristics.* National Center for Juvenile Justice, U.S. Department of Justice.

Struckman-Johnson, C. and Struckman-Johnson, D. (1994). Men pressured and forced into sexual experience. *Archives of Sexual Behavior*, 23, 93-115.

Thoennes, N. and Tjaden, P. (November, 2000). *Full report of the prevalence, incidence, and consequences of violence against women: findings from the national violence against women survey.* Washington DC: U.S. Department of Justice, National Institute of Justice, NCJ 183781.

Tjaden, P. and Thoennes, N. (2006). *Extent, nature, and consequences of rape victimization: findings from the national violence against women survey.* Washington, DC: US Department of Justice. Web. 24 May 2013 <www.ojp.usdoj.gov/nij/pubs-sum/210346.htm.>

U.S. Department of Health and Human Services. *Statutory Rape: A Guide to State Laws and Reporting Requirements: Summary of Current State Laws.* 2012. *HHS.* Web. 24 May 2013. <http://aspe.hhs.gov/hsp/08/sr/statelaws/summary.shtml>

Wolitzky-Taylor, K.B., Resnick, H.S., McCauley, J.L., Amstadter, A.B., Kilpatrick, D.G., and Ruggiero, K.J. (2010). Is reporting of rape on the rise? A comparison of women with reported versus unreported rape experiences in the national women's study replication. *Journal of Interpersonal Violence*, doi: 10. 1177/0886260510365869.

ABOUT THE AUTHOR

Dr. Rosemary Iconis is an Associate Professor with the City University of New York. She has written extensively for newspapers, popular magazines and professional journals on topics related to the health of both children and adults.

Contact Information

Dr. Rosemary Iconis
Queensborough Community College
of the City University of New York
222-05 56th Avenue
Bayside, NY 11364 - 1497